WINES AND VINEYARDS
OF SPAIN

WINES AND VINEYARDS
OF SPAIN

MIGUEL A. TORRES

Photographs: **ALBERT PUJOL**

English translation and additional material: **JAN READ**

Foreword by **JACQUES BERGERET**
Professor of the University of Dijon (Burgundy)

EDITORIAL BLUME Milanesat, 21-23 Barcelona-17

To my sister

First published english, 1982

ISBN 0-932664-27-X

© Miguel Torres, 1977
© Photography, Albert Pujol, 1977
Printed in Spain
B-6837 - 1982
Emograph, Barcelona

'Wine', in itself a history, science and art, is the subject of this book, to which Miguel Torres has dedicated so much time and care.

It is now twenty years since, as a young student at the University of Barcelona, he took his father's advice and went to Burgundy to study oenology.

Without doubt, the time that he spent in the capital of the ancient Dukedom left a deep impression on him and influenced his whole future. Eager to learn anything touching on wine production in different parts of the world, Miguel Torres, who has travelled widely and is an experienced taster, has never lost sight of the fact that to make wine of quality and character one must first establish a vineyard worthy of it. This is just what he has done in the magnificent region of the Penedès, where experimentation is the watchword. In a modern and well planned bodega, he carries out the vinification and maturation of his wines both with sound judgement and with the enjoyment of one who takes pride in work well-done, constantly seeking to improve them.

It is a pleasure for the writer of this brief foreword to praise the enterprise of his former pupil, a young oenologist with faith in his work. He hopes that this book will reach a wide audience and that it will interest and enthuse its readers, spreading the message that the world of vineyards and wine knows no frontiers.

Jacques Bergeret,
Professor of Oenology,
Dijon University,
November 1976.

AUTHOR'S FOREWORD

Three years have elapsed since the first Castilian edition of "Wines and Vineyards" appeared in Spanish bookshops. During that time many of my friends from abroad, largely English and American, have shown an interest in obtaining an English translation of the book. The task, however, has proved difficult and, in addition, it has been necessary to provide the foreign reader with more detailed information about Spanish wine-producers and their wines. As a viticulturist and vintner found this particulary difficult since any criticism or praise could have been interpreted as commercial bias which is quite contrary to the aim of the work.

The question of translating the text was solved thanks to the collaboration of my good friend John Reay Smith, who did a magnificent job.

Subsequently, however, I asked Jan Read, a real specialist in Oenology and Spanish Wines, for a technical revision of the text and wording, and to enlarge the chapter dedicated to Spanish Wines. Jan, being thoroughly acquainted with all the Spanish wine regions, accepted the idea with enthusiasm and carried out what I would consider an extraordinary task, one which I am sure will meet with the reader's approval.

Now all that remains is to hope that "Wines and Vineyards", in its first English edition, will be welcomed by wine lovers around the world. It is perhaps the first book on wines written by a Spaniard to cross our frontiers...

INTRODUCTION

For more than two thousand years the peoples living along the coast of the Mediterranean have drunk wine to quench their thirst, to accompany food and for simple enjoyment. Their art, history and literature are closely linked with wine; and their poets have sung its virtues. Its reds and golds have inspired our most famous painters; and in cathedrals and palaces, sculptors and architects have used the vine as a symbol.

Roman civilization has been called the civilization of wine; and its production and consumption were central to the life of those early Mediterranean settlements, whose culture was to spread throughout the world. When Christ elected to change wine into his own blood, he perhaps had in mind its importance as a drink to the Jewish community: 'And he took the cup, and gave thanks, and gave it to them, saying, Drink ye all of it: For this is my blood of the new testament, which is shed for many for the remission of sins.' For believer and non-believer alike, his mystical words brought the hope

A typical wine bar: Russkie's in London.

7

of salvation, and more than a healthful drink, wine has now become the means by which man is united with God and is indissolubly bound up with his very soul.

Today our society stands more than ever in need of wine: honest, sincere wine, which brings men together and helps them surmount the barriers of prejudice. Think of a banquet where the guests hardly know each other: to begin with, they are silent and awkward; they glance at the food or read and re-read the menu; they feel uncomfortable and ill-at-ease. But, as the wine works its alchemy, conversation flows, ideas expand, eyes sparkle, friendships flourish among the glasses. It is then that man's true nature is revealed. He is, after all, a sociable being; and to live, he must communicate, know that he is appreciated and feel that he is among friends.

So let us celebrate wine, realising that if it did not exist it would have to have been invented. Aldous Huxley knew this when in his *Brave New World* he erected a new civilization on the basis of the Utopian drug, 'Soma', and man will always need a 'Soma' to withstand 'the slings and arrows of outrageous fortune'.

When drunk in moderation, wine fulfills this purpose perfectly; and it seems likely that as long as there are men on earth, the vine will flourish. Year after year its complicated biological processes, still not fully understood, will continue, and it will offer its fruits as a tribute to human intelligence. Those tight clusters of grapes contain within them the essence and mystery of life, of the earth, the rain, the sun and man's labour.

CHAPTER I

My initiation into wine

Since the seventeenth century there has been a very real love for wine in my family; and the tradition has been handed down from father to son, I must, however, confess that at the tender age of eighteen I was not interested in the legacy of my forebears. At the time I was reading chemistry at Barcelona University, and though I raised no objection, I was somewhat disconcerted when my father announced that I was to go to France and study oenology at the University of Burgundy.

I was to leave behind many friends and memories, but from the outset I found the idea of going to a French university, and more than that, learning about French wines and vineyards, most exciting.

To begin with, I found Dijon, the capital of Burgundy and the seat of the University of Oenology —oenology is the science of wine and

The Church of Santa María in Vilafranca del Penedès, and the sign hanging in front of the Wine Museum.

is principally concerned with biology and chemistry— so different from anything that I had known at home that it took me some months to settle down. In those days Dijon was a closed community, jealous of its dignity and traditions; and the students lived in a world of their own. We had our own cafés, discothèques and restaurants, which, if not noted for their *haute cuisine,* were at least cheap.

Every two or three weeks the foreign students were invited out to lunch at the home of some local family, and some of those first meals were embarrassing. My French was still rudimentary and did little to help conversation; and my hosts often seemed remote and cold. However, there was wine to make things easier, and after the delights of an elegant Chablis, of an aromatic Pouilly-Fuissé, of the enchanting richness of a Volnay or of a distinctive Beaune, conversation became more animated. Suddenly I was no longer the foreign student invited for Sunday lunch; we had found something in common, something we enjoyed talking about. Communication had been established.

I spent two years at the University, mixing with students from France, from Algeria, Morocco and Tunis —the famous *pieds noirs*— and others from all over the world: from the United States, Australia, England, South America and Japan. Thursday mornings were devoted to the pleasant task of wine-tasting —and I must admit that it was the best attended and most successful class of the whole week. The tastings were usually conducted by our professor, Jacques Bergeret; and the object was both to analyze by taste the separate components of the wine and to fathom the country or place of origin, the grape and the age.

We also went on periodic rounds of the neighbouring *bodegas* (French, *chais* or American, 'winery'); and this was no problem, as we were living in the heart of Burgundy. I must confess that our primary interest was not in the installations, the vineyards, or technical information, but in secreting the odd bottle under the nose of our unsuspecting guide! Some adepts provided themselves with double-lined coats; and these 'poaching jackets', bulky as they were, enabled us to leave the *bodega* without being detected...

But in those days, when General Franco was still in power, for a student from Spain perhaps the most agreeable aspect of life at a french university was the feeling of personal freedom. Compared with Barcelona University, austere, old-fashioned and sombre, I found the University of Dijon modern, happy and efficient. Everything was allowed; non-attendance at classes was perfectly normal, there were no police attached to the university; the students could hold public meetings where they could speak freely and criticize what they did not like; and, of course, we could go to entertainments of any sort. In our own universities at the time taboos and prejudices were rampant, and the difference in the outlook of the students was most striking.

My final examination, the culmination of two years' of effort and study, did not present the same enormous difficulties as in Spain. I remember that not more than ten per cent of us had passed the examination in Chemical Sciences at Barcelona, the so-called *Común de Ciencias,* covering five subjects: Mathematics, Physics, Chemistry, Biology and Geology. To stand any chance of passing these exams meant nights of sleeplessness and study from April onwards; and the few who were successful were left worn-out and exhausted. It took a three months' summer holiday before one felt human again.

I worked hard at Dijon, but differently; and during the examination itself the students were allowed considerable freedom. The examinations at Barcelona were supervised by at least ten tutors and professors; talking was strictly forbidden; and we were not even allowed to go to the lavatories. At Dijon, a class of sixty students was invigilated by a single tutor —who fortunately occupied himself in reading his newspaper. I remember the frequent visits to the lavatories and the sensation caused among my fellow students by the *chuletas,* little *aides memoires,* scribbled, unscrupulously, I am afraid, on cigarette packets and match boxes. They were unknown to the French students in those days...

The birth of a wine; must pouring from the press.

I finally joined the family firm in 1962 and for several months worked exclusively on research in the laboratories and the introduction of foreign vines into our vineyards. Shortly before starting my military service I undertook my first bottling of wine. This involved decisions about which wines to use, how to blend them and supervision of the actual bottling process. It was my first important assignment in the production department, and I remember that some 40 000 bottles of white wine were carefully bottled and consigned to our deepest cellars, also that there was an argument with our old cellarman about the method of filtration. On his side there was the traditional 'We have always done it like this' and on mine the new doctrinaire ideas, reflecting my brand new qualifications as a French oenologist.

It was not long before I discovered my mistake; and it was one of the most agonizing moments of my life. I was in camp at Reus, completing my term as a recruit before taking my oath of allegiance, when my father descended on me. He had with him a sample case of that famous wine; and already, only a few weeks after bottling, the sediment was clearly visible. I was shaken to the core and deeply disappointed. According to my new-found technical knowledge it was impossible, but our old cellarman had foreseen exactly what

The Castle of Calafell de Dalt, vines in foreground.

would happen. It was a hard blow for my pride at the beginning of my professional career, but it made me realise that I must never set aside the traditions of a *bodega* which had been making good wine for centuries in favour of the techniques so recently learnt in France. I learned that one should always temper the more recent advances in the theory and practice of oenology with due respect for long-established tradition.

So I came to understand something fundamental to all good oenology —that wine is a living thing, subject to continuous change and evolution, and that there are no fixed rules. One cannot say that because a particular system or method is successful in Burgundy or Bordeaux that it will be equally applicable in Penedès. Our climate, soil and grapes are different; and further than this, each year and each harvest differs from earlier ones and poses its own technical problems. There are times when we seem to have perfected some technique and, because it has proved successful with one harvest, we imagine that it will become standard practice in the future —but experience goes to show that this is not so.

In succeeding years the sun is more or less intense, the rain more or less abundant, and sometimes the vines suffer from pests or .diseases; all these are factors which stamp each year and harvest with its own personality. They must always be studied and analyzed; the problems must be tackled in the light of past experience, but we must always be ready to adapt and modify, and above all to experiment, so as to abtain the best possible wine.

This is the fundamental mission of an oenologist; and although the variation between one harvest and another makes each wine a separate problem, herein lies the fascination and main attraction of his life. He knows that his work is never routine, that it is not enough to apply rules and formulae, but that he must continually create, give birth to new ideas, experiment, investigate and evolve, and so produce a great wine as the result of his labours.

CHAPTER II

A short history of wine

The history of wine is as old as that of the human race, and for this reason it has left its mark on the civilizations and peoples who have known how to make and appreciate it.

Prehistoric man most certainly knew how to make wine, and palaeontologists have discovered fossils bearing the imprint of grape-skins and pips left over from the pressing —*marc,* as it is called in France, or *orujo* in Spain. The earliest writings of man, such as the cuneiform clay tablets of Babylon and the papyri of ancient Egypt, contain many references to the fermented product of the vine.

The Bible would have it that wine was invented by Noah, but here, of course, we are in the realm of legend. Nevertheless, wine-making was well-established in the Middle East and parts of China by 3000 B.C., and the famous bas-relief from Ur, dating from 2500 B.C. and preserved in the British Museum, embodies scenes relating to wine. Ancient Chinese writings tell of a man, who was punished in

Bell-shaped Graeco-Italian jug of the third century A.D. (Museo del Vino, Vilafranca del Penedès).

Iberian wine jar of the third century A.D. (Museo del Vino, Vilafranca del Penedès).

2285 B.C. for blending true wine with that made from rice.

In Egypt, wine was used for the funeral ceremonies of its kings about 3000 years before Christ, and at the time of the Pharaohs one of the best-known vines was the Kankomiet grown in the vineyards of Rameses III (1198 to 1167 B.C.). The Egyptians introduced the labelling of wine, and some of the descriptions were very detailed. So, one of them runs: 'In the year 30, good wine from the well-irrigated land of the temple of Rameses II in Per-amon. Cellarmaster: Tutmes.'

The Bible mentions wine more than two hundred times, and the fact that Christ chose it for the most important ritual of the Christian faith is convincing evidence of its importance to the Jews of the time.

It was extremely popular during the period of Greek civilization, and to a certain extent the Greeks were precursors in the art of caring for wine. They perfected the amphora and introduced preservatives such as gum, resins and spices; even today resinated wine, *retsina,* is popular in modern Greece. The Greeks were proud of their wines and considered them an important part of their culture, as emerges from the story of Ulysses and the Cyclops, Polyphemus. When Ulysses and his companions were trapped in the giant's cave, that astute and daring hero offered the giant a skin of red wine. Polyphemus accepted it and became intoxicated, and it was thus that the voyagers were able to escape from his sinister cavern.

Dionysus, the Greek god of wine, was in fact more than the exaggerated faun of the Renaissance. The Greeks had explored the field of human psychology and created two gods, representing the poles of human life. Apollo, the god of light, was cold, temperate and intellectual, and his code of conduct, inscribed in the temple at Delphi, could be summarized as: 'Know thyself, and do nothing to excess.' His counterpart, Dionysus, was the god of the subconscious, of instinct, impulse and intoxication, and so came to be known as the god of wine —for it is wine that sets men free from cold reason and bares the inner being, or, as the Romans said: *'In vino veritas'*.

It was probably the Etruscans, a mysterious people thought to have come from Asia Minor, who planted the first vineyards in Italy; and at the time when Romulus and Remus were still being suckled by the she-wolf and the Eternal City was yet to be built on its seven hills, they were already planting vineyards on the volcanic slopes to the north of Rome. Wine soon entered its gates and with it the drunken orgies or *Bacchanalias* in which the Romans proved themselves more hardened topers than the Greeks —though, as Juvenal pointed out, there were some who were disgusted by the excesses of their decadent city.

When Julius Caesar conquered Gaul, the Romans first discovered wooden barrels —an invention of the Celts, who used them not for wine, but beer. The Romans soon realised that they were ideal for transporting wine, and both safer and more capacious than the classical amphorae then in use.

During the Roman occupation of Spain there were already many flourishing wine-producing districts, the best-known being Valdepeñas, Barcelona, Gerona, Valencia, Tarragona, the Balearic Islands and Betica (the south-west of Andalusia). In those days wine was one of the principal exports to Rome, possibly sent in payment of tribute; and in the museums of Rome one can see amphorae dating from the year 31 A.D. and labelled *Vinum Digatanum* —perhaps the forerunner of present-day sherry. We do know that in the province of Betica it was the custom to ferment and store wine in large earthenware jars called *orcae,* and the wines of Montilla and Moriles are still made in similar vessels today. It has been estimated that by the second century A.D. some twenty million amphorae of Spanish wine had been shipped to the city of Rome; and proof of this is the extraordinary artificial mound behind the British

Carthaginian amphora (Museo del Vino, Vilafranca del Penedès).

Nineteenth-century wine-press (Museo del Vino, Vilafranca del Penedès).

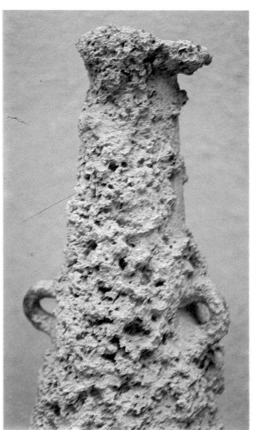

cemetery, the so-called Monte Testaccio, entirely composed of the fragments of broken amphorae. Two thousand years ago the River Tiber was navigable by ships carrying amphorae of oil, grain and wine; naturally many were broken during the voyage and the pieces were piled up to make this man-made hill.

Because Mohammed had forbidden his followers to drink wine, many of the Spanish vineyards were rooted up or simply abandoned after the Moorish invasion of 711 A.D. The extent of this disaster has perhaps been exaggerated; some wine was still made and the thirsty inhabitants resorted to a variety of tricks to evade the severe penalties of Islamic law. For, example, there is a story that a habitual drunkard was brought before the Moorish magistrate in Córdoba to be tried. In his wisdom, the judge called upon an official —who had been carefully briefed— to certify that the accused's breath smelt of wine. After exhaustive tests the official explained that, although the man's breath undoubtedly had a smell, it was difficult, if not impossible, to decide whether it was that of wine or grape juice...

For anyone interested in the history of wine, there is a museum unique in Spain and among the three most important of its kind in Europe, the Wine Museum at Vilafranca del Penedès in Catalonia. Here can be seen the remains of implements used for wine-making, carefully preserved as proof of the great antiquity of viticulture in Spain. There is a press dating from the fourth century A.D., together with Carthaginian amphorae of the first and second centuries and others from the Roman period. There are also wonderful examples of wooden presses, mostly from mediaeval times, and a most interesting set of tableaux dealing with wine and its harvesting at different periods in human history. On exhibition, too, are unusual paintings, ancient bottles, wine glasses, chalices, pictures, drawings and engravings.

The Reconquest in Spain, when the Moorish-occupied areas were slowly but surely overrun by the Christians of the north, saw the rebirth of the vineyards. This was largely the work of the monks, since wine was an indispensable element in the celebration of the Mass; and they laboured to cultivate vines around their monasteries to meet the need. Many of the most famous vineyards of today were first planted by monks of that period, as, for example, the Clos de Vougeot in Burgundy and the Priorato —from the name Prior— in Catalonia. Between 500 and 1400 A.D. Europe became the world centre for cultivation of the vine, and contemporary literature, poetry and art clearly reflected the profound influence of wine on mankind. By now it was the accepted drink with a meal —no doubt because of the unreliable and often tainted water of the time.

Just as civilization brought viticulture to Europe, so later it did to America; but the vine grew in America earlier than in Europe. When Leif Erikson and Columbus first landed in the American

Bodega in Vilafranca, c. 1930.

continent they found vines growing wild, and so luxuriant were they
that the Nordic sagas relate that Erikson named the region *Vinland,*
or the land of the vine.

Only twenty-six years after Columbus's first voyage, Cortés, the
Spanish conqueror of Mexico, embarked on the systematic planting of
vineyards, and wine henceforth became an important industry in the
New World. Cortés ordered every Spanish colonist in the region to
plant ten vines a year for each American native living on his land, and
they developed a variety known as *criolla,* grown in abundance as the
vineyards were extended in the centre and north of Mexico; it
produced fruit both for eating and making wine. Cultivation of the
vine spread so rapidly in the New World that the king of Spain feared
that the wines would compete with those produced at home and
called a halt, declaring all wine not imported from Spain to be
contraband. Although this measure was only partially effective, it
slowed production for a time.

With help from the Jesuits, the Spanish colonists penetrated as far
as the west coast of Mexico and the south of what is today the State
of California, and their successors, the Franciscans pushed further
north. As each new mission was founded, vines were planted in its
vicinity as a first step towards civilization. It was a Franciscan,
Father Junípero Serra, who founded the mission of San Diego in
1769. He planted selected vines, discovering that California was
especially suitable for viticulture, and his successors established a

chain of missions stretching from San Diego to Sonoma, the most westerly point on the famous Camino Real (The Royal Road). Vines descended from those planted at the time still grow today. The largest *bodega* was constructed at San Gabriel, close to Los Angeles; it was equipped with three wine-presses, and the original building may still be seen today.

Viticulture was also important in South America, although in Peru the *criolla* vine never produced wine of much quality, and it was usually distilled for making the spirit known as Pisco. Nevertheless, the acclimatization of better vines, especially in Argentina and Chile, made possible the production of excellent wines and laid the foundation of the modern industry, now famous for the quality of its wines, particularly those from Chile.

In France, a Benedictine monk, Dom Perignon, made a discovery in the seventeenth century, which revolutionized wine-making in the district of Champagne. The white wines of the region underwent a secondary fermentation, producing quantities of gas. Since the stoppers in use at the time were made of cotton or wax and were not air-tight, they were frequently ejected by the pressure inside the bottle. Dom Perignon accidentally discovered that the cork from Catalonia was a much better material for making a hermetic seal and used it with great success. He was then faced by a further problem, because the gas pressure was such as to shatter the glass; but he then persuaded the manufacturers to make bottles capable of withstanding pressures of some atmospheres. The result was astonishing. His wine had acquired a sparkle, and on tasting it he exclaimed: '*Venez vite mes frères, je bois des étoiles*!' ('Come quickly brothers, I am drinking stars'), Dom Perignon was tasting for the first time the wine we know today as Champagne.

At the beginning of the nineteenth century the district of Penedès was largely wooded or given over to wheat, and vines were not much cultivated. However, the growing demand for wine from the Spanish colonies overseas soon resulted in an extension of its vineyards, and the outbreak of phylloxera in France created a new European market for its delicious wines. It was the beginning of a new chapter in the history of wine.

The phylloxera, or *Phylloxera vastatrix* as it is known to botanists, is an insect 2 mm to 3 mm long, feeding mainly on the tender roots in the subsoil and producing incurable tumours. Unknown in Europe until the nineteenth century, it undoubtedly arrived when American vines were introduced for experimental purposes. The insect does not attack the tougher roots of the native American vines, such as the *Lambruscas* or *Rupestris*, but rapidly proved a scourge to the European vine, the *Vitis vinifera*. It first appeared in the north of France in 1863, spreading like an oil slick at the rate of some 30 to 50 km a year and constituting an absolute catastrophe for the

21

wine-growers of the period, since they knew of no way of combatting it. Later, most of them began grafting shoots of *Vitis vinifera* on to the rootstocks of American or wild vines; in this way the quality of the *Vitis vinifera* was retained in combination with the resistance of the American vine to the attacks of phylloxera.

Concurrently, the outbreak of phylloxera in France and the consequent progressive destruction of the French vineyards led to a virtual explosion of planting in the Penedès; the demand grew and grew; not only overseas countries, but the whole of Europe wanted its wines, and even the remotest parcels of land were pressed into service. From this period date the first terraces, strips cultivated on the mountainsides to make the maximum use of land. Although most of these terraces have now been abandoned because of the enormous labour of cultivating them, one can still see them —for example, along the national highway between Barcelona and Vilafranca del Penedès (Término municipal de Ordal).

In the late nineteenth century 80 per cent of the vines cultivated in the Penedès were red varieties, and the total area of the vineyards was 20 000 hectares. Later, there was an enormous increase in the percentage of white vines, dating from the time when production of sparkling wine by the Champagne process was begun in the area. According to contemporary records, exports of wine from the Province of Barcelona amounted to 1 273 389 hectolitres in 1880. A little later, in 1884, the dreaded and long-expected phylloxera finally reached the Penedès, and here, as in the other wine-growing areas of

Terraces in the High Penedès.

Europe, it ruined many families who had traditionally depended on the vine. The determination and skill of the experts of the day nevertheless resulted in the development of grafts resistant to the scourge, and in a few years the vineyards were restored, this time permanently.

The quality of the wine produced by man during much of his history would probably be considered very poor by the exacting standards of today —it will be recalled that the Greeks and Romans used disagreeable products such as pitch and resin as preservatives. Until the nineteenth century most wine was drunk young during the year of vintage because of the difficulty of keeping it, and the wines were usually oxidised or vinegary. It was only in exceptional circumstances that it could be aged in barrel or that wine bottled under ideal conditions would last for any length of time.

It is also understandable that for reasons of climate cultivation of the vine most prospered in the warmer regions of the Mediterranean, since the large amount of sugar in the must gave rise to wines with plenty of alcohol and good keeping properties. It is very likely that the Jerez wines of the eighteenth century were even then of high quality, and possibly similar to those of today; but, on the other hand, the Burgundy or Penedès of that time could certainly not compare with the present-day wines.

One could say that oenology, a combination of biology and chemistry applied to the study of wine, was born with Pasteur; and oenology is in some degree the medicine of wine. In these days wine is not made in laboratories, but it is studied and analysed in them, so as to devise means of maintaining quality and avoiding diseases and accidents; and the whole crux of making fine wines is the amalgam of modern techniques and tradition.

In the huge plants making wine for everyday consumption, it is now-a-days fermented in great metal tanks of up to 500 000 litres capacity, and the aim is to make the wine as quickly as possible; but in many *bodegas* the old family traditions, modified in the light of modern practice, still survive. Whether manufactured for mass consumption by industrial methods, or lovingly elaborated by craftsmen, wine is and will be, man's true companion through the ages, for an honest wine stirs the heart and soothes the spirit.

The wine harvest (stained glass by Pablo Boada).

CHAPTER III

World-wide cultivation of the vine

Of the plants comprising the large family of *Ampelidaceae*, the noblest belong to the genus *Vitis*. All bear grapes, but of the ten separate species found in Asia and sixteen in America, only some ten produce fruit from which wine may be made. By contrast, there exists in Europe only one unique and exclusive vine, *Vitis vinifera,* from whose grapes are made the greatest wines in the world.

As explained in the previous chapter, before the discovery of America vines were cultivated only in Europe and the Middle East, though it is possible that vines were grown in China, but only on a small scale.

By the fifteenth century several regions of Spain, Italy, France, Germany, Austria and Greece, together with various countries in Eastern Europe, Russia and the Middle East, were already making well-known wines. Until then the main areas of production were those around the Mediterranean, where the mild climate and large amount of sun favoured cultivation; and wines with high alcohol content are easier to preserve, and therefore to transport and commercialize.

When the Conquistadors took the first vines to America, always those traditionally cultivated in Europe and the Middle East and of the species *Vitis vinifera,* it heralded a new epoque in the history of world viticulture. The early Spanish settlers were nevertheless surprised to find in some areas of America plants with leaves like those of the vines they had known in Spain; they grew wild and their fruit had an unpleasant taste —hence the name under which they are scientifically classified: *Vitis rupestris.* Other similar species are known as *Vitis labrusca, Vitis rotundifolia* etc. *Vitis vinifera* adapted particularly well in certain parts of Mexico and Southern California and was mainly cultivated by the missionaries, who needed wine for celebrating Holy Mass.

The Geography of Vine Cultivation

Why is the vine not grown in such countries as Norway, Sweden or Guatemala? The answer lies in the existence of well-defined geographical limits, and, as can be seen from the map, it grows best along a belt lying between the latitudes of 30° and 50° in both hemispheres. The determining factor is the climate: for example, in the northern hemispheres, regions lying above 50° are too cold; and the vine requires a minimum heliothermic degree (the heliothermic degree measures the total amount of solar radiation received each year). But there is also a maximum, and below 30° of latitude the climate is too hot, and cultivation of the vine is not possible.

Detailed examination of the map shows that it is the areas in the cooler part of the belt which produce the great table wines. The noble vines which produce the finest table wines (Bordeaux, Burgundy, Rhine, Penedès, Rioja and the rest) require cold winters and moderately hot summers.

Consider a line dividing northern Portugal, crossing Spain at the

Castellet in the Lower Penedès.

50°

30°

30°

50°

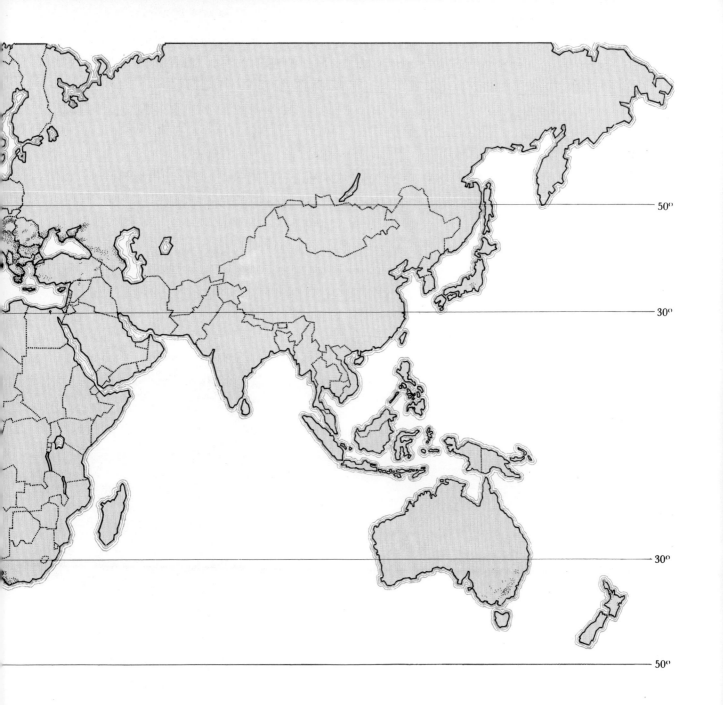

50°

30°

30°

50°

THE AREAS OF CULTIVATION LIE MAINLY BETWEEN LATITUDES 30° AND 50°

29

latitude of Burgos and Tarragona and extending across central Italy. By and large, the area lying between this line and latitude 50° North produces the best table wines of Europe. The only exception is perhaps the South of France, the famous Midi, where the climate would permit the making of good wine, but where cultivation has been orientated towards mass production of wine for blending and everyday consumption.

Below this line lies the whole central part of Spain, where good wine is made in regions such as Valdepeñas or Utiel-Requena, but most of which is produced for everyday drinking.

Finally, for reasons of climate, the south of Spain and southern Italy make the great apéritif and dessert wines. In these sunny areas the grapes yield musts very rich in sugar and the wines are correspondingly high in alcohol. They include such world-famous growths as sherry, Montilla-Moriles and Málaga, and, in Italy, Marsala and Lachrima-Christi.

The Vine, the Climate and the Soil

A vine more than fifty years old.

The High Penedès in winter.

From the technical standpoint, three factors determine the characteristics of a wine:

1. The climatology, dependent on the latitude and geographical situation of the area of production.

2. The vine or stock, either a noble vine producing a small quantity of high quality grapes, such as the Pinot in Burgundy, or an ordinary vine with a large yield of inferior must, such as the Aramon of southern France.

3. Finally the soil. By this is meant the composition of the ground on which the vines are grown —and what is curious is that there are sometimes great variations between one parcel of land and another in the same vineyard. The wine from separate parts is different, though the vines are the same and grown in identical climatic conditions. The discrepancy arises because the soil may alter considerably within a distance of a few metres; sometimes a road forms a natural boundary separating vineyards, and one finds that on one side, because of the more suitable composition of the soil, a better wine is produced than on the other. For example, in Burgundy, the main road between Beaune and Dijon bounds the vineyards making the great wines of the Côte de Nuits. The wines from the left side of the road, travelling from Beaune to Dijon, are all grands crus, while those from the right are generally of lower quality.

An Aramon vine.

A Pinot vine.

The vine is an extremely robust plant, capable of withstanding low temperatures in winter and great heat in summer, and requires a minimum of water and mineral elements to survive. Paradoxically, the best wines are made from vines growing in barren, arid land, unsuitable for most other crops; and this is why in Spain a larger area is devoted to the cultivation of the vine than in any other country of the world. Up and down the country, more than 1 700 000 hectares of land are dedicated to it.

It is quite extraordinary to see how the vine fights for survival in any sort of terrain: it flourishes in the stony ground of the Côtes du Rhone; on the steep volcanic scarps of Tenerife; on the cold slopes of the Rhine valley; and in the rocky and savagely beautiful terraces of the lower Penedès, where it produces some of the best red wine in Spain. It triumphs where no other crop could survive, thrusting its roots deep into the soil to seek the mineral nourishment and moisture, without which it could not live.

The Vine World-wide

Soon after the introduction of the vine to Mexico and Southern California, its cultivation was extended to South America; and today vines are grown in Chile, Argentina, Brazil and, on a smaller scale, in other countries of the South American continent. They have also been acclimatized in South Africa, Australia and New Zealand, and even, with great difficulty, in Japan. Russia has recently become a prolific producer of wine and now ranks next to Spain in importance.

Today, then, the vine is grown the length and breadth of the world and is the source of an infinite variety of wines, apéritifs, brandies and liqueurs. Each district, each region can and should ensure that its wines retain their own individual style, that they are not imitations of those from older, more famous regions, and that they possess a personality and character of their own marking them out from all others.

Ploughing Roman-style; an image from the past.

CHAPTER IV

The creation of a vineyard

It is difficult to understand why so many books on wine, both Spanish and others, fail to devote a few pages to the vine. Except for text books written for the serious student of oenology, they often overlook the fact that the vine is worthy of as much attention and study as the wine itself.

Even in the commercial field there is a certain lack of interest: the vine is the farmer's problem. Most Spanish *bodegas* buy their grapes from independent growers at the current market price; some take temporary leases of vineyards so as to exercise technical control over their working and the quality of the fruit; and others again confine themselves to buying wine in bulk from private producers or cooperatives, relying on careful blending and ageing to obtain the desired style. There are, however, firms in the Penedès and other areas, which undertake the whole process of wine-making: harvesting, fermentation and ageing.

I have noticed that most of the visitors to our *bodegas* are extremely interested in everything to do with the vines. It is, of course, very pleasant to tour the carefully-tended vineyards in the comfort of a car, and at harvest time they enjoy sampling the sun-ripened grapes; but the vine means much more than this, for it is from it that the quality of the wine proceeds. As a child, I well remember my father's remark to a party of foreign visitors, who had made the rounds of our bodega and had been duly impressed:

> "Gentlemen, good wine is not made here,
> but out there in the vineyards."

And, in fact, oenology can do nothing with grapes that are lacking in quality, are diseased or degenerate, or have not been properly protected from decay or insect pests.

The vine is a plant which has been better and more intensively cultivated than any other on earth; it is an astonishing 'factory', not only looking beautiful and producing fruit, but also playing a part in the fight against atmospheric pollution.

The Life-cycle of the Vine

Some vines live healthily for fifty years or more, and year after year they follow the same predestined life cycle.

In November, they shed their leaves; and the stocks, twisted and stylised, form a gaunt frieze against the cold sky. It is a sad landscape, sometimes cloaked in a silent white mantle of snow, worthy of any painter. Winter is a long interlude, when the vines, their vital functions at low ebb, wait and bide their time.

In February, the vine awakes and thrusts out tender new shoots. The skilled farmer prunes the weak and straggling; and the shorn vines gesture towards the sky, as if anticipating the arrival of spring.

With the first warmth of April, the sap rises anew; a whole botanic laboratory is set in motion; the first young leaves unfold, and the vineyard is soon fragrant with the scent of flowers.

Their role is fundamental, and they must be fertilized if life is to continue. Flower shapes ans scents attract bees, wasps and other insects; it is they, and sometimes the wind, which deposit pollen

Pruning the vines.

Emergence of the bud.

The bud opens.

The flowering of the vine.

Pollination.

The berries change colour.

The vine in autumn, before the harvest.

inside the flowers, so quickening them. Formation of the fruit then begins.

In July, the first clusters of grapes appear, waxy white and miniature; if nature is kind and the weather favourable, they will slowly swell, gain colour and ripen in the sun.

October is harvest time, a season of songs and long-rewarded labour, when the grapes are picked and taken to the *bodega.* Under the lengthening autumm sun the vineyards glow copper and magenta, a whole symphony of subtly different tones and colours. Once again, as from time immemorial, the vine has fulfilled its natural purpose and prepares to lie dormant until another spring.

What is a Vine?

Botanists tell us that it belongs to the family *Ampelidaceae,* genus *Vitis,* order *Rhamnales,* subclass *Polypetalae,* class *Dicotyledones,* subtype *Angiospermae* and type *Phanexogamae.* By definition it is a plant comprising roots, stem or trunk, and branches or shoots, on which the leaves are hung by petioles. The grape berries form around small twigs.

The roots often reach a depth of ten to fifteen metres, growing

41

Note the difference between the leaves of Vitis rupestris (Left) *and* Vitis vinifera (Right). *The former have smoother, more rounded edges.*

downwards until they find the moisture essential to the plant, and at the same time absorbing the necessary mineral and nutrient elements, which will later be carried to the leaves by the sap. These leaves are usually hexagonal in shape and vary according to the type or variety of the vine. By inspecting the leaf the oenologist is able to determine the type of stock under examination; between them, the location of the veins, the greater or less indentation of the leaf, the type of petiole and the colour will provide him with the necessary information.

All the species of vine cultivated in Europa and the Middle East belong to the family *Vitis vinifera*.

Chlorophyll

Much has been written about chlorophyll and its special attributes, and it has been said that it fulfills in plants the same function as

Bunches of ripe Xarel-lo grapes.

haemoglobin in the blood of higher animals —but what is chlorophyll and how does it work?

It may be defined as an organic substance of complex chemical structure, found in the sap of the vine and other plants. Green in colour, it acts by collecting energy from the rays of the sun and transferring it to the leaves, where photosynthesis takes place.[1]

---

[1] In connection with photosynthesis, it may be explained that there are two forms of natural process:

a) Those which liberate energy by changing complex molecules into simpler ones, as in the digestion of food by the stomach or in alcoholic fermentation.

b) Processes which absorb energy, building up simple molecules into the more complex. This is the case with photosynthesis. Molecules of carbon dioxide gas (CO_2) and water (H_2O) are used to create molecules of acids and sugar. The required energy is provided by the green pigment chlorophyll, which captures it from the rays of the sun.

Morphology of the leaf, showing the pattern of veins.

Section of a black grape.

Section of a white grape.

It is scarcely twenty years since its mechanism was finally unravelled, and it is so complex that there is little point in going into it more deeply here.

In effect, the leaves are the laboratory where the process is carried out, and the resulting products are gradually stored up in the bunches of grapes.

Making a Vineyard

A new vineyard must always be planted in sterilized land free from infection, since the vine is specially susceptible to viral diseases causing infectious deterioration and cryptogrammic sickness, as a result of which roots rot and the plant dies.

The preparation of the land begins about January, when it is dug over deeply and disinfected.

Prior to the late nineteenth century the method of planting was to insert into the ground a cutting of a vine shoot from the local variety of *Vitis vinifera*. Once established in the earth, the shoot sent out roots, and three years later the young plant would produce its first harvest.

This simple procedure no longer sufficed once the European vineyards had been ravaged by phylloxera. As has been described in Chapter II, it fed on the roots of the vine, and all the means then known of exterminating pests proved useless. The only vineyards which survived were those near the sea; the phylloxera cannot tolerate saline soils, and in vineyards subject to winter flooding it is drowned.

Grafting the Vine

Vine-grafting. Left: *the cut or incision;* Centre: *inserting the graft;* Right: *application of the protective covering.*

Faced with this disaster, man had to find a solution if cultivation of the vine was to continue. The origin of phylloxera, previously unknown in Europe, was urgently investigated; and when it was discovered that it had come from America, expert viticulturalists went to Mexico and the United States, where they found that the wild American vine, of a different family from *Vitis vinifera,* was well-able to co-exist with the dreaded pest. Enquiries continued until a practical solution was found.

The roots of the American vines, already in existence before the arrival of Columbus, were hardier and stronger and could successfully withstand the attacks of the insect. The experts therefore recommended to the hard-pressed growers that 'the local *Vitis vinifera* be grafted on to a stock of the American vine previously acclimatized to the soil.

From then on the grafting of vines has become accepted practice in all European vineyards. It does not materially affect the quality of the fruit, and even today no more effective and economical method of fighting the phylloxera has been discovered.

Grafting is done in the year following the planting of the American vine, and grapes will not be produced until three years later.

Staking the Vine

Spanish vines pruned in traditional fashion (*poda en vaso*) do not need supporting wires, but in Burgundy and on the Rhine, and also when vines from these regions are grown in Spain, support is required. Delicate vines, protected and supported by stakes, are pruned differently by the so-called Guyot method. This form of cultivation is undoubtedly very expensive, calling for 12 km of wire per hectare —quite apart from the cost of posts and labour— but the higher quality of the fruit makes the investment worthwhile.

A vineyard pruned en vaso *(Spanish-style)*.

Tilling the Soil

The vine is a very long-lived plant, producing abundant harvests for twenty to twenty-five years, after which the yield slowly drops. It is usual to replace vines after twenty-five years, so that during his lifetime a farmer will see the passing of three generations on his land. However, if it is to grow and flourish, continual care and cultivation are necessary.

Surface tillage is carried out with the object of breaking up and aerating the soil, keeping down weeds and protecting the vines against frosts. With the approach of winter comes the autumn ridging, and the earth along each row is heaped up against the stocks as a protection against frost and to provide for drainage, and at the same time minerals and fertilizers are dug in.

In the spring, the stocks are uncovered by removing the earth and laying it between the rows. A mechanical cultivator is used regularly throughout the year to eliminate weeds, which, apart from absorbing minerals, are a source of infection from mildew and other diseases.

The Harvest

By June the fruit is still extremely acid. How is it that this acidity gives way to the delicious sweetness of fully ripened grapes?

Preparing the surface of the vineyard.

Acids are produced in the grapes through the agency of chlorophyll, when, as a first stage, carbon dioxide is absorbed from the atmosphere and combined with water —in this way it performs a true job of anti-pollution. The summer sun helps convert these acids into sugars, pectins and all the other substances which go to the very complicated composition of the must.

The timing of the harvest is decided by an acceptable balance of sugars and acid in the grape, and this differs according to the district and type of vine.

Until recently harvesting has been carried out entirely by hand, but in California and Australia it is now being performed by automatic harvesters capable of doing the work of forty men.

Although the development and improvement of these machines is being closely studied in the Penedès, it is considered that they break up the bunches of grapes too brusquely and that their use should be postponed for some years.

Diseases of the Vine

It would be inappropriate to go into detail about the numerous dangers and diseases to which the vine is prone, but very briefly these include:

An automatic harvester.

a) Climatic risks, such as hailstorms, frosts and floods, about which there is little the viticulturalist can do.

b) Attacks by pests and fungi, against which the viticulturalist can usually take protective measures by dusting with sulphur or spraying with a copper solution.[1] Reference is made to decay or *Botrytis* in the next chapter.

Effects of a hailstorm. Above: *after a few hours.* Below: *seven days later.*

¹ With a base of copper sulphate, this is specially indicated in dealing with that most damaging of fungal infections, mildew, which can wipe out a vineyard in its entirety. In some years as many as twelve to fifteen sprayings are required to prevent such attacks.

A vineyard inundated by torrential rain.

Protective spraying of a vineyard. ▼

CHAPTER V

Making and maturing white wines

Once the grape has reached maturity, the first stage in the making of a wine is over, and the quality of the end product is entirely predictable. If the grapes have been picked from select varieties of vine carefully cultivated for moderate yield, and if the weather has been kind, one may hope that they will give birth to a fine wine, If, on the other hand, the vine is an ordinary type or the yield is excessive, or if, simply, the rain and good weather have not come at the right time, then the quality of the fruit will be suspect.

Choosing the bunches of grapes.

At this point it is important to understand the difference between the work of a craftsman seeking quality, and bulk production undertaken with a view to quick profit and aiming at maximum output, not only from the vineyard, but also in the making and elaboration of the wine.

Grapes are normally gathered when they are perfectly ripe, but there are exceptions to this rule worth mentioning, especially those wines described as 'over-ripe'. The best-known are Sauternes, from the French district of that name in the south of Bordeaux, and the rather similar wines from the Moselle and Rhine, such as the 'Beerenauslese' and, most famous of all, the 'Trockenbeerenauslese'.

The condition of over-ripeness is brought about by the combined action of the sun and the wind in drying out the fruit, with loss of weight and a consequent increase in the amount of natural sugars in the must. At the same time the acidity is lowered, and the wine that emerges is of a very special character. A principal element in this process, responsible for the exceptionally delicate flavour of such wines, is the presence of the fungus known as *Botrytis cinerea* ('The Noble Rot'). Occuring naturally in the soil, it is deposited on the skins of the grapes, and its development is encouraged by warmth and humidity.

The vine yields its fruits.

The fungus puts out thin filaments known as *mycelia,* which

penetrate to the heart of the berry and, quite apart from the increase of sugar content through loss of water, bring about a reduction in the amount of acid, particularly tartaric, and the formation of glycerine. Because of this the wines are characteristically very smooth. Harvesting takes place about December or January; by this time the loss of weight is as much as 50 per cent, and the grapes present a sorry appearance, being dessicated and covered with mould. The fermentation of the wines poses special problems, and they are difficult to keep.

Wines of this type are not produced in Spain for reasons of climate, and in any case the demand for wines such as Sauternes has long passed its peak. Sweet white dessert wines are not much drunk now-a-days, and the market for them is very limited.

It should be stressed that in ordinary vineyards *Botrytis* causes decay and damage to the harvest; and it is only in the above-mentioned areas, and in special conditions of humidity and temperature, that its appearance is welcome.

Transporting the Grapes to the Bodega; The Pressing

The method of carrying the grapes to the *bodega* depends on the available resources and the type of wine to be made. Those destined

Emergence of the marc *from the press.*

for ordinary wines are transported in bulk, by tractors, in tubs, or in lorries fitted with tarpaulins. For quality wines, it is essential to use small wicker or plastic baskets, so that the grapes arrive unbroken at the *bodega* for crushing —a pre-condition for obtaining a healthy must. If must is produced during transport there will be premature fermentation, resulting in poor flavour and the spoiling or infecting of fermentation.

Arrangements for the reception of the grapes at the *bodega* depend on the type of wine that is being made. In modern installations for the production of ordinary wine (*vino corriente*) the principal aim is to obtain maximum output from each machine with the minimum of labour. In general, the stalks will be removed from the grapes, and they will be crushed and pressed in 'continuous' presses, capable of high throughput and requiring little attention. The resulting musts are separated according to type; those from a 'continuous' press are always of inferior quality, and in the Penedès such wine may not be sold with a *Denominación de Origen* (corresponding to the French *Appellation Controlée* and guaranteeing the quality and place of origin of the better wines).

The lay-out of a plant suitable for making good quality white wine is described in more detail in Chapter VI. The baskets may be emptied into the crusher mechanically or by hand, but always with care; and pressing is carried out, mechanically or pneumatically, in horizontal presses —the important thing being that pressure is

Hydraulic presses (Cavas Codorníu).

57

applied gently and progressively to the mass of crushed grapes, so as to obtain must of good quality. Great care must be taken with skins, stalks and pips; in a 'continuous' press their bruising incorporates bitter elements into the must, and this is why wines made in this fashion are always inferior.

The Must before Fermentation

As soon as the must leaves the press it is channelled into collecting chambers and allowed to rest for a period of twelve to forty-eight hours, during which any small stones or solid material brought from the vineyard settle out and remain as a sediment at the bottom of the container. This material is later removed by racking (or decanting), and the must is left clear. To further this operation the containers are previously sterilized by burning in them a little sulphur, so ensuring a completely sterile and aseptic atmosphere. Some of the sulphur dioxide produced in this way is retained in the must and both sterilizes it and facilitates the process of decantation.

As regulations stand, sulphur dioxide is the only foreign matter added to wine, white or red, and then only to ensure that the containers are completely sterile. Its use dates from Roman times and is freely permitted by every country in the world. The amounts are extremely small, and exhaustive tests have shown that it has no harmful effects. Sulphur forms part of human tissues and is present in much of our daily food.

Wine Yeasts

With the production of the must the real biological process of making the wine begins. It is barely thirty years since the fermentation of wine was fully understood, and it was a complete mystery until Pasteur started his investigations some hundred years ago. I do not wish to weary the reader with technicalities, but simply to explain the origin of wine, one of nature's miracles; and more detailed information is given in the footnotes.

The ferments or yeasts of wine are microscopic organisms scientifically described as fungi[1] ; they exist naturally in the soil of

---

[1] Those occuring naturally in wine belong to the families of *Endomiceteae* and the *Cryptocaceae*. Of the different sub-groups of these families, those most commonly found in the must are the *Saccharomyces* and the *Kloekera*.

the vineyard and, carried by insects or the wind, are deposited on the skin of the grapes, where they may be seen as a dusty, greyish-white film, which disappears when washed with water. The larger part of this dust is composed of yeasts and bacterias, which, as will be seen later, play a fundamental role in the making of wine. Without yeasts there could be no fermentation, and without fermentation there would be no wine. The yeasts are incorporated into the must while the grapes are being crushed.

The Discovery of Yeasts

Systematic study of fermentation began in 1669 when Sylvius de la Boe discovered that the gas produced in the process was carbon dioxide; and in 1682 the biologist Becher made another important step forward in establishing the difference between fermentation and putrefaction, which, though also a natural process, is no more than a progressive degeneration. In 1780 the French chemist Lavoisier found that during the course of fermentation the sugar in the must was mainly transformed to alcohol and carbon dioxide, and on this

Must pouring from the presses.

discovery he based his well-known principle that: 'In nature nothing is created or destroyed; it is only changed.' According to this theory, the amount of alcohol and gas at the end of fermentation must therefore be equal in weight to the sugars originally contained in the must.

In 1803 Thénard carefully investigated the deposit formed in the fermented liquid, discovering that it was analogous to the yeast in beer; from this he deduced that the fermentation of wine was also the work of yeasts, though the eminent biologist was unable to say whether the organisms were of animal nature or simply nitrogenous.

Another French chemist, Gay-Lussac, carried out an experiment in which grape juice was kept at 100° C (the boiling point of water) for several weeks. He demonstrated that fermentation did not then take place and concluded that this was because the yeasts essential to the process had been deactivated.

The father of modern oenology was the illustrious Louis Pasteur,

who in 1878 put forward the idea of yeasts as living organisms.[1]
During a thorough investigation of all types of fermentation,
especially that of wine, he uncovered the fundamental role of oxygen
in alcoholic fermentation and established the following theory:

1. In the presence of air the fermentation of the sugars of the must
   gives rise only to carbon dioxide and water.

2. In the absence of air the same sugars produce alcohol and carbon
   dioxide (alcoholic fermentation).[2]

Fermentation

A few hours after the grapes have been pressed and the must has
been decanted and channelled off, fermentation begins. The yeasts
multiply extremely rapidly and very shortly reach a population of
millions per cubic centimetre.[3] As a result of fermentation, alcohols,
principally ethanol, are formed and reach amounts of 7 to 16 per
cent by volume, according to the type of wine and the district where
it is produced.[4] Certain higher alcohols also appear, together with

---

[1] At the time this theory was disputed by the German, Liebig, who accepted
only the idea of diastases, the chemical molecules which instigate fermentation.
It was Büchner who finally reconciled the two theories by concluding that yeast
contains the diastases.

[2] According to this, if the fermenting must is left in continuous contact with air,
the fermentation will degenerate and the alcohol, together with all the aromatic
elements that make up the wine, will be lost. Fortunately, the same carbon
dioxide produced at the beginning of fermentation forms a protective blanket,
preventing the fermenting must from coming in contact with air; thus, in the
absence of oxygen the second type of fermentation takes place. Although the
final products of alcoholic fermentation are basically alcohol, esters, aldehydes
and other aromatic components of wine, the intermediate stages are extremely
complicated, and one must turn to modern oenology for an explanation. It is,
in fact, only recently that Meyerhoff and Warburg have demonstrated that these
intermediate stages of alcoholic fermentation are similar to those taking place in
the human body during the digestion of sugars.

[3] An interchange takes place through the walls of the yeast cells; and the sugars
in the must, essential to this vital phenomenon, are absorbed. Part of the energy
released in this process is retained; and the different components of the wine,
mainly ethyl alcohol, are discharged as by-products. It is the diastases, very
complicated substances secreted by the yeasts, which catalyse the process
through an intricate chain of chemical reactions.

[4] There are also infinitesimal traces of methyl alcohol, normally not in excess of
0.1 gm/litre.

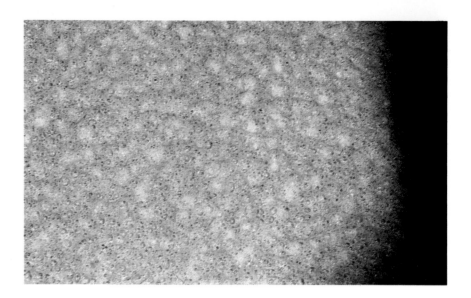

The surface of the must during fermentation.

complex esters which are largely responsible for the bouquet of the wine.[1]

Fermentation also introduces vitamins into the wine, mostly of Group B;[2] it is, however, low in Vitamin C and does not contain enough for human needs. Other biological constituents are most useful to the body, as will appear later in a chapter about its medicinal properties.

Carbon dioxide is given off continuously during fermentation, and if one puts one's ear to the vat an incessant rumble of bubbles can be heard from the inside. A great variety of vessels is used, ranging from small wooden casks to huge stainless steel tanks of up to 500 000 litres or more. As might be expected, large tanks are forbidden for quality wines with *Denominación de Origen.*

Making White Wines of Quality

For centuries the best white wines have been made in small containers, and even today use is made of wooden barrels with

---

[1] During fermentation the wine is enriched with iron, copper and tannins, and also with glycerine, tartaric acid, malic acid, lactic acid (found in milk) and citric acid (found in oranges and lemons). Esters may appear in amounts of as much as 1 gm/litre; another important constituent are amino acids, which play an important role in the physiological processes of the human body.

[2] B_1 (thiamin), B_2 (riboflavin), pantothenic acid, pyridoxine, biotin and mesoinositol.

capacities of not more than 600 litres. More recently stainless steel tanks have been introduced and represent the ultimate advance in the techniques of fermentation. Today they are considered ideal vessels, because stainless steel is aseptic, dissipates heat quickly and does not transmit unwanted flavours to the wine. It must, however, be clearly understood that these containers are used only for fermentation and not for maturing the wine; it is essential (in the case of red wines, at any rate) that this should be done in oak casks. Fermentation normally lasts from one to six weeks, depending on the temperature and type of wine —the colder the outside temperature, the slower the fermentation, because the activity of the yeast is inhibited.

Once fermentation is over the wine is racked (or drawn off) to separate it from the lees, containing the yeasts. Next, it is matured in oak barrels —if appropriate to the type of vine and style of the wine. Some white wines are not matured in oak, but stored in suitable containers and bottled after a few months, so preserving

Rows of cement vats (Masia Olivella).

their freshness and fruitiness and avoiding oxidation and loss of aroma. A white wine aged in oak for too long deteriorates in quality and suffers from oxidation, which imparts a yellowish colour and rancid taste.

White wines are never matured in wood for more than twelve to twenty-four months, when they are clarified and filtered prior to bottling.

Bottling and Preparatory Treatment

Before they are bottled wines must be clarifield and filtered so as to obtain maximum purity and brilliance. As the word implies, clarification involves the addition of natural coagulents to carry down any solid particles which would otherwise make the wine cloudy[1].

The wine is next filtered, and thin sheets of cellulose are used to obtain the complete clarity essential in all bottled wines. As an alternative to filtration, centrifugation has recently been introduced; and this high speed rotary process removes all solid particles, leaving the wine clear and brilliant.

Some *bodegas* also freeze and pasteurize their wines. Although these treatments are perfectly legal and do not effect the composition, they should nevertheless be avoided with fine wines, which may be debilitated and impoverished.

Pasteurization in particular destroys all living matter in the wine, making difficult its ageing in bottle, so essential for the development of a rich bouquet and flavour. Its fundamental aim is to eliminate all living organisms in the wine by heating it to a high temperature and is the process used for killing yeasts and bacteria in milk. Wine is much more complicated, and its delicate balance can be upset by such violent treatment. Nevertheless, pasteurization is a practical and economical way of preserving everyday wines and of preventing biological changes in the bottle.

The purpose of freezing wine is to accelerate the deposition of tartrates, substances occuring naturally and formed by the combination of tartaric acid with calcium and potassium. They look

---

[1] The usual clarifying agents are isinglass, white of egg and gelatine. They are first dissolved in a little water and, when added to the wine, form clots that are precipitated within a few hours, leaving the wine clear. The use of these agents is perfectly legal, and since they are completely precipitated and subsequently removed, it is not a question of adding a foreign substance to the wine.

Preparing the filter.

much like crystals of sugar and can often be seen in bottles of wine which have been chilled for too long in a refrigerator. They do not in any way spoil the taste, but their appearance is unattractive. Refrigeration before bottling is a safeguard against later complications, but if a few minimal precautions are taken tartrates ought not to appear; and with properly matured wines the treatment is unnecessary, because years of ageing get rid of tartrates gradually and naturally.

By-products

The pressing of white wine gives rise to certain by-products (skins, stalks and pips), known in Spain as *orujos*. When dried, they can be used for the distillation of alcohol or dug into the soil as manure. The French name for *orujo* is *marc,* and its distillation yields the well-known *eau-de-vie de marc,* similar to the *aguardiente de orujo* from Galicia.

Types of White Wine

The differences between individual wines stem from the vines: their fruit will be more or less aromatic, possess more or less body and a greater or smaller amount of acidity; and the characteristics of the wines made from them will be similar.

In the Penedès the types of vine most often used are the Parellada, the Macabeo and the Xarel-lo, in descending order of importance. Vines have also been introduced from other parts of Europe: for example, the Gewürztraminer from Alsace, the Chardonnay from Burgundy and the Riesling from Germany. The *Consejo Regulador* (the local agency of the *Instituto de Denominaciones de Origen*) permits the planting of 'noble' vines from other districts of repute, but their produce must be submitted to the *Consejo* for examination and tasting before they are approved.

The type of wine also depends upon the method of pressing; for example, wine from a mechanical crusher is always lighter and has less body than that from horizontal presses. Wine from a 'continuous' press is rougher, more acid and more bitter, and is unsuitable for development as a quality table wine. Other factors influencing the end product are the temperature and types of yeasts used during fermentation.

Finally, sweet or semi-sweet wines are made by removing the yeasts before fermentation is complete and while the wine still contains a small amount of natural sugar from the must. After separation of the yeasts by centifugation, by clarification or especially by filtration, when they are trapped in the thin sheets of cellulose, the sugar remains in the wine.

Analyzing the new wine.

CHAPTER VI

Making and maturing red and rosé wines

The Making

The processes of making rosé (*rosado*) and red wines are basically the same as for white wines; the composition of the musts is almost equivalent, the fermentation is controlled by yeasts and ferments, and the final product differs little from white wines. What, then, are the essential differences between the making of white and red wine?

In practice, they can be reduced to two:

1. For red wines the grapes are pressed without their stalks.
2. Unlike white wines, the rosés and reds are fermented in contact with the skins.

These differences are shown schematically in the diagram overleaf. First, in the case of white wines the stalks, or woody stems of the grapes, are pressed with the grapes as a whole; but in making rosé or red wines they are removed when the grapes are first crushed, and a destalking machine is usually coupled to the crusher (see footnote, page 72). A special pump then forces the resulting pulp or must, together with the skins and pips into the fermentation vat.

The presence of the skins and pips is essential with rosé and red wines, because the natural pigments which give the wines their colour are found in the skins. White wines should not be unduly yellow and they are made as light in colour as possible, but the pigments are needed for the reds and rosés, and they are extracted slowly during fermentation. It is easy to show that the colour of red wines is obtained from the skins, simply by squeezing out the deep red colour of any black grape between the fingers. The colour of red wines in fact derives from pigments of two types, the red anthocyanins and dark yellow tannins; and the alcohol produced during fermentation, together with the rise in temperature in the vats, helps the gradual absorption of the pigment by the wine.

Separation of the stalks.

Red wines are fermented at higher temperatures than white, sometimes as high as 30°C, and larger vats are generally employed, often with capacities of 4000 to 20 000 litres —and even more in the case of everyday wines. During fermentation the skins float on top of the must, and the sodden mass in called the *sombrero* or 'cap'. During the early stages this 'cap' is sprayed with must pumped up from below, a process known as *remontado*. Once the skins have coloured the wine, they are removed; the longer they remain in contact with the must, the deeper the colour they impart; and rosé wines normally require only twenty-four hours. This is how genuine rosé wine is made, and the doubtful practice of blending red and white wines never achieves the same quality, although at a quick glance the colour may look much the same.[1]

In most wine-growing regions no correction of the must is normally required, but in colder areas, as for example Burgundy or Bordeaux, it sometimes proves necessary to add sugar to the must to increase the alcohol content of the wine. In Germany, this is called *Verbesserung,* meaning 'improvement', but the practice is generally

---

[1] Until the beginning of the present century it was standard practice to leave the stalks in the must during fermentation, with the result that the wine was sharper and bitterer and also more difficult to mature. Destalking is normal now-a-days and gives rise to smoother and pleasanter wines.

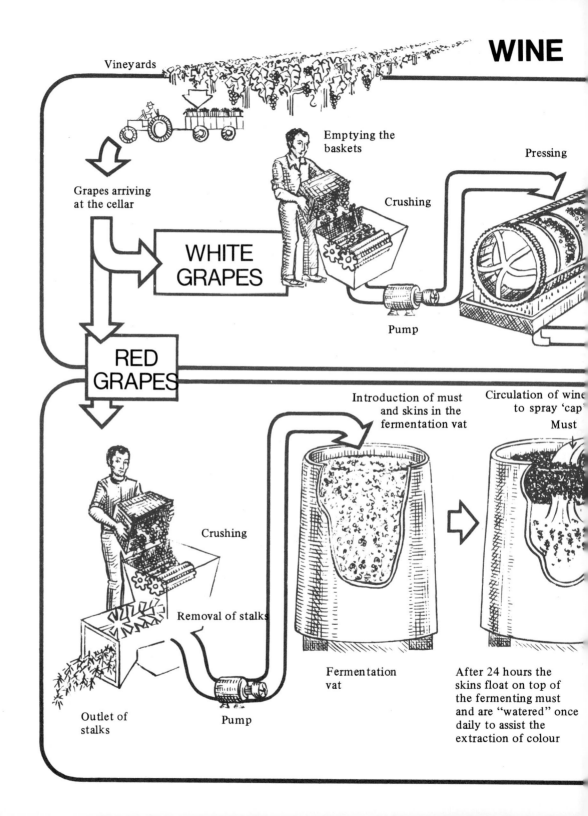

WINE

Vineyards

Emptying the
baskets

Pressing

Grapes arriving
at the cellar

WHITE
GRAPES

Crushing

Pump

RED
GRAPES

Introduction of must
and skins in the
fermentation vat

Circulation of wine
to spray 'cap'

Must

Crushing

Removal of stalks

Outlet of
stalks

Pump

Fermentation
vat

After 24 hours the
skins float on top of
the fermenting must
and are "watered" once
daily to assist the
extraction of colour

72

PRODUCTION

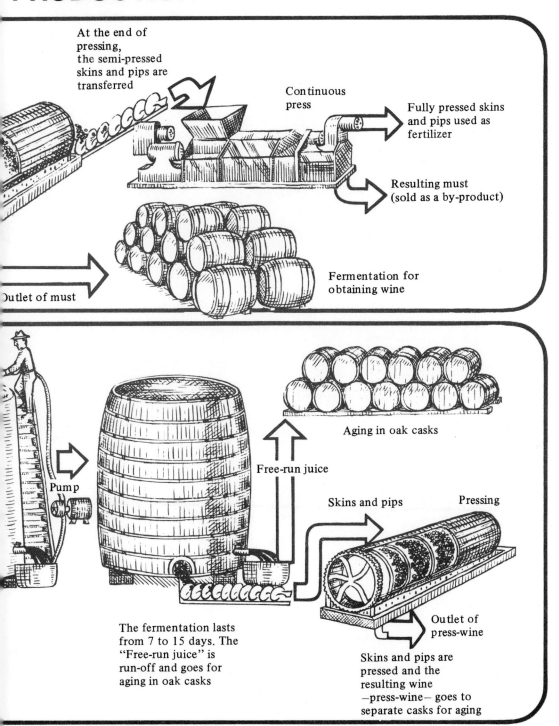

At the end of pressing, the semi-pressed skins and pips are transferred

Continuous press

Fully pressed skins and pips used as fertilizer

Resulting must (sold as a by-product)

Outlet of must

Fermentation for obtaining wine

Aging in oak casks

Free-run juice

Pump

Skins and pips

Pressing

Outlet of press-wine

The fermentation lasts from 7 to 15 days. The "Free-run juice" is run-off and goes for aging in oak casks

Skins and pips are pressed and the resulting wine —press-wine— goes to separate casks for aging

73

The surface of the must during fermentation.

known as Chaptalization from the name of the French chemist, Chaptal, who pioneered it. In most parts of Spain the musts are well-balanced enough for Chaptalization to be unnecessary.

In some very cold regions the must is excessively acid because of the lack of sufficient sunshine, and small doses of calcium carbonate are added to the wine to counteract over-acidity. This practice, which in no way harms the wine and is known as 'corrective', is permitted by the laws of different wine-producing countries.

Secondary or Malo-lactic Fermentation

After alcoholic fermentation, red wines are transferred to a second vat, the wine from the first pressing being known as *vino de yema* (literally, 'yolk of wine'). The mass of skins and pips, the so-called *marc,* remaining after the *vino de yema* has been decanted off, is pressed again, and the wine so obtained is known as *vino de prensa.*

It is usually richer in tannin and pigment than the wine from the first pressing, and the cellarman decides on a judicious blend of both, with due regard to the characteristics of the harvest in any particular year.

The biological life of the wine has just begun, for as soon as the yeasts disappear, the bacteria take over. They too are found naturally in the soil of the vineyards[1] and are responsible for the malo-lactic fermentation, which continues for some weeks. At this stage it is most important to keep a constant watch on the condition of the wine, and the moment the malic acid has disappeared the bacteria must be removed by decanting and filtration, since they become malignant if allowed to remain in longer contact with the wine and initiate changes prejudicial to its quality. Continuous analysis and the

---

[1] Like the yeasts, the bacteria are deposited on the grapes in the form of microscopic dust, and they are activated immediately on pressing, when the skins are mixed into the must. There are benign and useful bacteria in wine and also some that are malignant and spoil the quality. Those that appear at the end of alcoholic fermentation are normally benign and are known as malo-lactic bacteria. Their function is simply to transform the malic acid in the must to lactic acid, also found in milk and yoghourt. Lactic acid has a smoother and more delicate flavour than malic; hence the malo-lactic fermentation improves the wine and makes it softer and silkier.

The remontado *(circulation of the fermenting must).*

Checking the colour of the wine during racking.

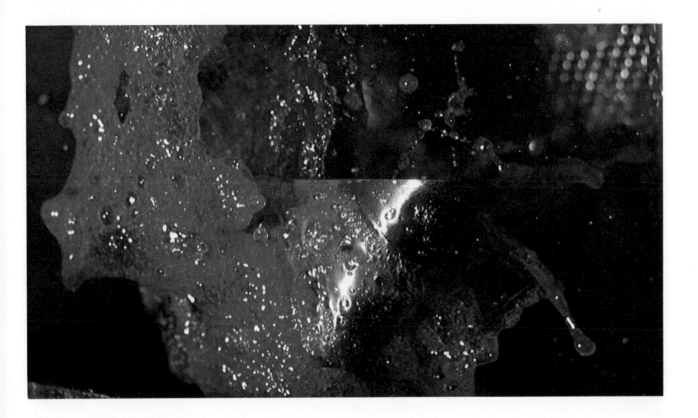

The variegated shades of the must.

employment of modern techniques such as microscopy, paper chromatography and dosage with volatile acid, enable the oenologist to make healthy and well-balanced wines.

The Maturation of Red Wine

Once malo-lactic fermentation is complete and the wine has been suitably racked and filtered, it is ready for ageing in oak. Some wines are clarified with gelatine before being matured, but other wine-makers prefer to do this after the wines have been matured in oak. Red wine is always matured in oak containers, whether they be small casks with a capacity of 200 litres or large vats of up to 100 000 litres. A great range of vessels is used, of many sizes and dimensions according to the district and local practice. Everyday wines are not matured in oak, but are simply racked and stabilized and then stored in tanks of metal or cement until they are bottled or sold in bulk.

Generally speaking, the more expensive the wine, the smaller the cask in which it is matured, and the owners of most *bodegas* prefer to use oak from the eastern part of the United States or from central France, especially the famous Limousin oak. While the wine matures in wood it undergoes a moderate degree of oxidation from air entering through the pores, but the quantity is small and it is sterilized in its passage through the wood. Recently the price of oak has become almost prohibitive, and in 1976, for example, a 300-litre cask of Limousin oak cost 11 000 pesetas (about £ 75 or S 150). This high cost markedly increases the price of the wine.

As it matures, red wine improves, and its intense violet colour takes on tones nearer brick-red, while the smell changes considerably, losing part of the aroma of the grapes and of fermentation and acquiring the more refined bouquet typical of a maturated wine.[1]

Maturation in oak usually lasts for a period of eighteen months to three years, depending on the type of vine and the harvest; longer maturation tends to impoverish the wine, and it shows its age, becoming 'tired'. From time to time the wine is racked so as to get rid of precipitated solids, and is in this way refined and prepared for final bottling.

---

[1] The change in colour is usually caused by the precipitation of anthocyanins and the progressive emergence of the yellower tones of the naturally occurring tannins, which together produce a brick-red.

A nineteenth-century cellar for the maturation of wines in casks.

Before this is done, it is usual in most *bodegas* for wines from different vineyards and vines, and also of different ages, to be blended, so as to maintain a typical style. Some *bodegueros* consider that blending is the most important part of wine-making and select with the utmost care the types of wine to be mixed and the most appropriate moment for doing so. Older wines are not normally as fresh and fruity as younger ones, but, on the other hand, young wines lack the complex bouquet and flavour of the more mature; and the addition of a small quantity of young wine often imparts freshness and fruitiness without spoiling the character and other qualities of the older. Nevertheless, I personally, am a firm believer in bottling wines originating from a particular vineyard and single harvest —though naturally these are wines made for an instructed public, appreciative of the differences arising naturally in wines produced from one year to another.

Maturation of Rosé and Red Wines in Bottle

As opposed to the reds, it is unusual for rosé (*rosado*) wines to be matured in oak, and they are bottled while still young and fruity, normally during the year following the harvest.

Does wine improve in the bottle? This is certainly true in most cases, but there are people who think that, once bottled, the wine stops developing. Perhaps there has been, and still is, a confusion with brandy and liqueurs, which do not age once they have been bottled. Whereas a 10-year-old brandy means a brandy that has matured in wood for ten years, and always will be a 10-year-old brandy, a bottle of wine can in time become a bottle of twenty, thirty or even more years of age and is labelled as such. There is an enormous difference in the wine at the time of bottling and twenty years hence.

Not all wines improve with age, and in fact no wine goes on improving for ever. Each reaches its peak at a certain age (just when, is, of course, a matter of personal opinion), depending on the original vine, the way in which it was made, and so on. In general, white wines are at their best earlier than reds, and everyday wines soon after bottling —in fact these wines ought not to be kept long, because in all probability they will not improve. It is rare for any white wine to get any better after it has been in bottle for three years, while certain red wines —for example, those made from the Ojo de Liebre— reach their peak after fifteen years.[1]

---

[1] The longer a red wine takes to reach its best, the better it will be. It is also true that the longer the time taken to achieve perfection, the longer will the wine

Very few wines remain in good condition after more than thirty years. Sooner or later all wines become vinegary or downright rancid, and some wines more than a hundred years old, such as those sometimes sold at the famous auction rooms of Christie's in London, are little more than museum pieces. However, it is usually not so much a question of the wine being kept too long, but of being drunk too young. To prevent this, many wine-makers keep their bottles in the store for several years before releasing them. In matters such as these, as in others, the lover of good wines must find out for himself which *bodegas* he can trust —particularly in regard to the year of vintage and other details printed on the label. It is impossible to impose controls which can guarantee the exact truth of such information, so that it is a question of relying on the integrity of houses with a reputation for making fine wine. As a general rule it is sensible to buy a white or rosé wine as young as possible, and a red

---

remain at its peak before beginning to deteriorate. As a general rule —and, of course, there are exceptions, but in my experience it applies in most cases— a wine will remain at its best for about half the time it took to reach this point, and then twice as long again before it is undrinkable. For example, white Parellada wine which has reached its optimum two years after it has been made, will remain at its best for another year, will then slowly decline for up to four years, and at seven years will be too old. However, an Ojo de Liebre or Garnacha wine will take six years to attain its peak, will remain in perfect condition for three years, and will not begin to deteriorate until fifteen years after the vintage.

Bottling wine.

wine not less than three or four years old. Never believe a label stating that the wine is of the 1928 vintage —if this were true, it would certainly be long past its best.

In conformity with current wine legislation in Spain (*El Estatuto de la Viña, de Vino y de los Alcoholes*), labels must state the contents of the bottle in cubic centimetres and also the alcoholic strength in degrees (i.e. percentage by volume). Nevertheless, it should be borne in mind that this is only an indication of alcohol content; and, in any case, a wine is no better for being high in alcohol —the reverse is often the case. The present tendency is to drink wines of moderate strength, between 10° and 12°, which can be enjoyed at a business lunch without the after effects of sluggishness, sleepiness or undue exhilaration...

The choice of wines is a large and important subject and it will be dealt with in a later chapter, but, in connection with the colour of wines, the normal rule is that the deeper the colour and the more intense its range of tones, the longer it can be kept. This implies that rosés should be drunk soon, not more than six months to a year after being made, the light reds over a period of five to ten years, and that only the great red wines, those with great richness of colour, should be kept longer.

Are there Sweet Red Wines?

Although the great majority of red wines are completely dry, there are exceptions; and the Priorato wines are an example. In certain years they are so rich in natural sugar that some remains in the wine after fermentation, and they are perhaps more suitable as apéritifs or dessert wines than for drinking with food.

Some red wines are sweetened with *mistelas,* syrups made by adding alcohol to the must, so cutting short the fermentation. These fall into the category of dessert wines, though they are also particularly suitable for making *sangría.*

Red wines are the very foundation of oenology; if the whites delight the taster with their elegance and finesse, it is the reds that engender an endless range of styles and flavours, depending on their origin, vines and year of harvest. In addition, from the point of view of health, red wine is particularly to be recommended for daily consumption, and is the most popular type all over the world.

CHAPTER VII

Keeping and serving wine

The Sommelier

The cup bearer or *sommelier* is the survivor of a picturesque
mediaeval tradition and, with his silver cup and leather apron, he is
still a most important dignitary in expensive restaurants. It is said
that in days gone by he also carried a bunch of keys at his waist,
since it was only the most trusted servant who had access to the old
wines, kept under lock and key in deep cellars by his master.
Poisonings were not infrequent at that time; it was the *sommelier's*
duty to taste the wines before serving them to his liege lord, and he
was lucky if he did not die in agony. Whether or not this is the real
origin of the *sommelier,* as they say in Italy, '*Se non è vero, è molto
ben trovato*' ('If it is not true, it is a happy invention').

Keeping Wine

Anyone really interested in wine should try to arrange for a small
cellar, or at least a few wine racks, to preserve and store his chosen
bottles. The ideal is a cellar or room below ground, free from violent
changes of temperature during the year; and wine keeps best at an
even temperature of 15° C. Failing this, one should choose a room
that is as cool as possible, with a certain degree of humidity and
without windows facing the setting sun. Avoid storing wine near
things with a strong and unpleasant smell; I have myself come across
a restaurant where petrol had been spilt in the cellar and given its
flavour to the wine. Noise, light and high temperature are wine's
worst enemies. There should be as little light as possible; always
avoid daylight, using a low-power electric bulb instead.
  Bottles of table wine are always binned horizontally, so that the
corks is kept wet. Otherwise it will dry out, allowing air to enter the

The binning of bottles horizontally.

bottle; and the wine will then oxidize and smell musty. On the other hand, bottles of apéritif wine, brandy or liqueurs with metal caps or corks with milled tops should be kept upright.

Preparing the Wine

It is best to get out the bottles the day before, and white or rosé wines should be cooled in the refrigerator for two hours before they are opened. Red wines should be taken to the dining room well beforehand, so as to come to room temperature, and uncorked an hour or two before they are served. As a general rule, the older the wine the longer it should remain uncorked, to allow for full development of bouquet and flavour.

In a restaurant, it is sensible to order red and white wines at the same time and to have them uncorked together, the whites for immediate drinking, and to allow time for the reds to 'breathe' before the arrival of the main course.

As regards temperature, it is recommended that the whites and rosés should be served between 6° C and 10° C, cold but not iced. Red wines are served at room temperature, but, as already explained, they should be allowed to come to temperature slowly; rapid heating, on top of a stove or in warm water, should always be avoided and is harmful.

Serving Wines

The following rules may be helphul:

1. The glasses. Glasses should always be transparent and uncoloured so that the clarity and colour of the wine can be appreciated; and it goes without saying that metal or pewter goblets should in no circumstances be used. Always refuse coloured or opaque glasses; the use of green glasses for white wine has no justification in theory or practice, and in any case deprives one of the pleasure of admiring the colour. Make sure that the glasses are odourless; they must be throughly rinsed and dried with a clean and very dry cloth. Check personally that they have not picked up any unpleasant odour before being brought into the dining room.

   For preference, choose balloon or tulip-shaped glasses, curving inwards at the top, since these retain the aroma of the wine and allow one to savour it to the full.

2. Show the bottle to your guests; a good wine lends distinction to your table and is a compliment to your friends.

3. Cut the capsule below the rim of the bottle so that when the wine is poured it does not pick up small particles of lead, which are bad for the digestion and can give the wine an unpleasant taste.

4. Clean the neck of the bottle with a napkin, inside an out, before and after drawing the cork. Examine the cork and smell it carefully; if it is damaged or smells of mould, the bottle should be rejected.

5. Pour the first few drops into a separate glass, as they may contain fragments of cork. Before it is served, the wine must be tasted;

Stages in the cutting and removal of the capsule. (Restaurant Orotava, Barcelona).

and in a restaurant the wine-waiter will first offer it to the host or the person he thinks best-qualified to judge, often the senior member of the party —and this is sometimes an honorous duty, even for the professional.

The important business of tasting the wine only too often develops into a meaningless ritual. On occasion, so little of the wine is offered that it is impossible to form a correct impression of the bouquet; and the glass should be filled to a third, so that by gently swirling the contents, the taster can judge nose and flavour. After that, a small sip is all that is needed to check the quality, and a nod of approval to the wine-waiter will allow him to serve the guests and finally the host.

An experienced taster will usually signify his approval simply by smelling the wine, as an expert can detect whether it is corked or vinegary by this *coup de nez* alone. The temperature is checked by feeling the bottle, and no more is required than the sense of touch.

At home the procedure is somewhat different; after showing the bottle to his guests, the host will taste the wine himself, and if it meets with his approval will then serve it to his guests. This, for the host, is the moment of truth: a few remarks about the provenance of the wine, its knowledgeable tasting and deft serving are all signs of the connoisseur.

6. The glasses should be only half, or at most three-quarters filled, so that the fragrance of the wine can be savoured by rotating them. After filling each glass, the neck of the bottle should be wiped with a clean cloth to avoid spilling drops on the table.

7. Fine red wines, the *grandes reservas,* should either be decanted or the bottle should be opened and served in a cradle, so that it remains in the horizontal position it has occupied in the cellar, without disturbance of any sediment.

8. Each bottle of wine, even of the same type and vintage, is different and should be separately tasted to avoid unpleasant surprises.

9. Some arbiters of 'good taste' would have it that the bottle should not be left on the table; but a fine wine is a work of art, worthy of admiration. A well-designed label adds distinction to the table, and in enjoying the food it is always pleasant to glance appraisingly at the bottle. One should remember the years of effort spent in growing and harvesting the fruit and the care lavished by cellarmasters and oenologists on what, over the years, has become a living, enchanting nectar.

And is not each label in itself a work of art? Not only does it describe the wine, but is the embodiment of the *bodega* and the owner who has made it; rarely does a label that is cheap and in bad taste adorn a bottle of good wine. It has been said that a wine reflects the personality of its maker; and the label is a foretaste of pleasure to come. The bottle should most certainly not be removed, either at home, for practical reasons, or in a restaurant; the diners should drink the wine in their own good time, and it is many times preferable that the bottle should be at hand and that glasses should not be overfilled than, as often happens in restaurants, they remain empty until the waiter reappears and fills them to the brim. In a good restaurant with an attentive wine-waiter it is permissable for bottles to be placed on a side-table; but they should always be left so that the labels, with information such as the year of vintage, are visible.

10. As has been seen, wine is a living substance, developing, maturing and improving with the passage of time; and no-one should be surprised if, after a period, a deposit appears at the bottom of the bottle. It is caused by the slow precipitation of tartrates and colouring matter, and one should take care not to shake the bottle and disturb it. If the wine is poured carefully, any sediment will remain in the bottle.

Serving wine (Restaurant Vía Veneto, Barcelona)

How Long Should Wine Be Kept?

Rosé wines should normally be drunk while they are still young and fruity, and there is therefore nothing to be gained by keeping a bottle for more than six months.

White wines can usually be kept for a maximum of one or two years; after this they grow yellowish, tend to acquire a maderized (or sherry-like) smell and become less fresh and fruity.

Red wines, on the other hand, can and should be kept longer; some have a life of twenty, or in exceptional circumstances, thirty years. It is impossible to lay down a hard and fast rule, but when buying several cases of a red wine, it is a good idea to taste it every six months and to note one's impressions in a small book. The wine will get slowly better over the course of time until improvement stops, at this point it should be drunk within a year.

To Be Avoided at All Cost

It is regrettable that mistakes are constantly made in the serving of wine, some because of inexperienced staff, and others because of the need to serve too many tables in a short time, or as a result of basic misconceptions as to the real function of wine.

A. Mistakes in Getting Ready the Bottles

1. Cutting the capsule above the rim of the bottle or pulling it off completely.

2. Careless shaking of the bottle, especially when the wine is old.

3. Turning the bottle when drawing the cork; what ought to be turned is the corkscrew.

4. Serving a vintage red wine immediately after withdrawal of the cork.

5. Failing to smell the cork before serving the wine; a bad cork can ruin the best wine.

6. Failure to wipe the neck of the bottle carefully with a clean cloth.

7. Using coloured glasses. They must be uncoloured and tulip-shaped; a coloured glass is simply a sign of bad taste.

B. Mistakes in Serving Wine

1. Filling the glasses more than three-quarters full; it is better to fill them only half.

2. Mixing wines of different types. For example, most of the diners may choose a dry white wine, and the others a sweet white wine. It is easy to confuse them unless the precaution is taken of using distinctive glasses for the sweet wine and instructing the staff accordingly.

3. Mixing different vintages of the same red wine. If during dinner the chosen vintage runs out, the host should be informed and the glasses changed; a change of vintage is always important and must be pointed out. The label should always specify the year, especially in the case of a red wine.[1]

4. Serving a white wine after a red. This is beyond the pale —except in the case of a sweet dessert wine served at the end of the meal. With the *hors d'oeuvres,* soup or entrée one may drink a rosé or *fino* sherry, but never a red wine unless it is to be served throughout the rest of the meal.

5. Serving a red or rosé wine iced; this will simply mask the flavour.

6. Serving a red wine (other than a red *vinho verde*) straight from the cellar; it must *always* be brought to room temperature.

7. Failure to taste each bottle which is served. That the host has accepted the first does not mean that he should not sample subsequent bottles.

8. Leaving the glasses empty; the practical and courteous solution is to leave the bottle on the table within reach of the guests.

---

[1] In the interests of a consistent product, as in the Rioja, some growers prefer to 'type' their wines, labelling them 3° año ('third year'), 5° año ('fifth year') and so on. This runs counter to oenological tradition, since one of the pleasures of drinking wine is to discover the differences between different vintages, and 'typing' should be restricted to everyday wines. The year of vintage is the birth certificate of a wine and should be displayed clearly on the label. The possessor of a cellar registers the passage of years with pleasure, since it denotes the improvement of his wine. A 'third year' bottle is anonymous and not worthy of his care.

9. Serving wine during and after the sweet —'just to finish the bottle'. Unless someone asks for it, a table wine should be removed after the cheese to make way for dessert wines such as Muscatel, sherry, Málaga or liqueurs.

Deterrents to the Appreciation of Wine

It is often difficult to pass an opinion on a wine because of the scant consideration with which it is served. Nothing is more common than to smoke a cigarette with an apéritif and also between courses at table —this, despite the well-known fact that tobacco affects the senses of smell and taste, preventing proper appreciation of food and drink. Smoking at table shows unpardonable lack of consideration for the other guests. When enjoying the subtle bouquet of a delicate wine, nothing can be more annoying than a thoughtlessly directed puff of smoke.

Cigarette smoking is clearly injurious and is fortunately falling into disuse in Western countries, where advertising has been curtailed and every packet must bear the warning: 'Smoking is harmful to health'. Thanks to well-directed educational campaigns, more and more Americans are giving up tobacco; smoking is forbidden in elevators, in trains and aeroplanes, and is no longer considered chic or an adjunct to the ego. At banquets and dinners guests are now-a-days often requested to refrain from smoking during the meal and to wait until coffee is served —hardened smokers can always retire to the lobby between courses, if they must.

At the same time, there does come a moment for tobacco, with the coffee and liqueurs, when a good cigarette or an aromatic cigar from Havana or the Canaries is acceptable.

Briefly to summarize the things which hinder the appreciation of wine, they include:

1. Tobacco.

2. Apéritifs high in alcohol, which blunt the palate for delicate wines. This is the moment for Champagne (in Spain, 'cava') or dry *fino* sherry.

3. Vinegar, especially in salads; it may be replaced by lemon juice.

4. Chocolate.

5. Metal goblets or coloured glasses.

6. Overpowering perfumes; some women (and men too!) charge the atmosphere with their toiletries.

7. Overheated rooms; restaurants often resemble Finnish sauna.

Changes in Wine during Storage

Remember, as already mentioned, that wine must be kept well away from things such as petrol, diesel oil, solvents, paints and industrial oils.

Assuming that conditions in your cellar are suitable, only two kinds of changes can occur in bottled wines:

A. Physico-chemical Changes

These include problems caused by oxidation or the appearance of tartrates.

The formation of tartrates (see page 64) is a natural process and is encouraged by marked changes of temperature. For instance, a consignment of white or rosé wine, bought during the summer and exposed to cold during the winter, will precipitate crystalline tartrates, looking much like sugar. They do not affect the quality of the wine, but one should ask the wine merchant to replace the bottles and then find a more suitable place to store them.

Oxidation is likely to occur when the bottles have been kept in hot surroundings, perhaps in the kitchen or near the heating system. In such conditions the corks dry out and the wines become oxidized or maderized, losing their freshness and often turning yellow or throwing a dull, brownish deposit. Bottles exposed to the sun in shop windows or show cases should be replaced every two to three weeks to avoid problems of this sort.

B. Biological Changes

These relate to the wine becoming vinegary or sour and to renewed fermentation.

A wine turns sour or vinegary when it is attacked by the acetic bacteria found naturally in red wines; an oenologist should know how to eliminate them by racking, filtration and by taking other precautions during maturation.

Re-fermentation is caused by yeasts (usually *saccharomyces oviformis*) similar to those active during the original fermentation, which the cellarman has carelessly left in suspension in the wine prior to bottling. They produce emission of carbon dioxide, accompanied by clouding of the wine and a later precipitation of solids. Wine that becomes vinegary or shows signs of re-fermentation should be returned to the merchant.

These are problems affecting bottled wines; wine in bulk —except when of high alcoholic strenght— should not be stored in barrels,

Tartrates in the wine after shaking the bottle.

butts or vats, but should be bottled as soon as possible, as it will otherwise be subject to major changes.

The wine-lover's cellar should be confined to bottles of good wine, with perhaps a small cask of choice old Priorato or oloroso sherry, since these do not normally pose any storage problems.

CHAPTER VIII

Wine and medicine

Since the early days of human civilization wine has been drunk with food, and it was not long before its medicinal properties were recognized.

It was a basic element in the pharmacology of the Egyptians, Greeks and Romans, probably because it is relatively stable, containing as it does alcohol and organic acids. The mediaeval alchemists were well aware of its uses and inherited from the Arabs the technique of distillation and of making 'the spirit of wine or water of life'. The distillation of wine was common practice in the Charente district of France by the seventeenth century and in the Penedès from the eighteenth. In those days spirits of wine proved most useful to doctors in preparing their prescriptions and potions; because of its high alcohol content it was an excellent solvent, would keep indefinitely and was biologically sterile.

Although the medicinal value of wine and spirits of wine was fully

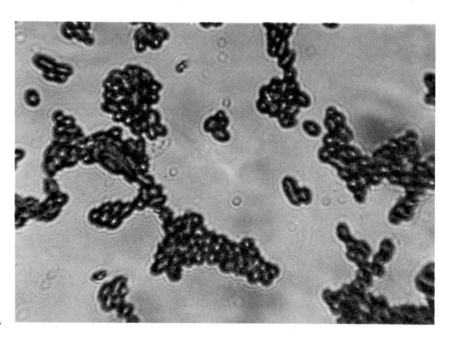

The wine yeasts.

recognized and they were used on an empirical basis, little was known about the many constituents or their function and properties. It was not, in fact, until the time of Pasteur that wine was studied scientifically, and well into the twentieth century before its physiological properties were fully understood.

The reputation of wine as 'the milk of old age', a tonic, appetizer, healthy beverage and sovereign remedy has been enshrined in a multitude of saws and proverbs; and without pursuing this, it is worth mentioning that verbal traditions, handed down from generation to generation, often have a long-forgotten basis in fact. Old people in the Penedès still recall that during cholera epidemics one of the prime precautions was to avoid water and drink nothing but wine. This still holds good today, since the cholera bacillus cannot survive in a moderately strong alcoholic medium such as wine.

From the cave-dweller to the modern executive, man has always been a prey to fears and tensions and felt a need to alleviate them. The caveman cornered by a tiger was under the same stress as the mediaeval warrior exposed to the hazards and dangers of some risky campaign; and across the ages man has resorted to wine as an escape from his anxieties.

But wine has other medicinal uses, though like any drug it is harmful if taken in excess —and in this it resembles morphia, aspirin and even water. Because of its agreeable taste there is perhaps more temptation to abuse it, but fortunately this does not happen too often and is no reason for overlooking its many other benefits; and of these the most important is that it so much contributes to human happiness.

Contra-indications

A normal adult can drink a half to a litre of wine a day, depending on how active he is. A sedentary worker should not drink more than half-a-litre, but a labourer engaged in heavy manual work or a freely-perspiring athlete may safely consume up to a litre. This, however, applies to table wines of moderate alcoholic strength (11°); and consumption of apéritifs, whisky and liqueurs must also be taken into account in assessing how much alcohol the liver can eliminate without danger to its delicate tissues. As a rough guide, an apéritif is equivalent to double its volume of table wine, and whisky and liqueurs to four times the amount: for example, 50 ml of whisky are the equivalent of 200 ml of wine. It must also be borne in mind that it is more difficult for the system to assimilate distilled alcohol than wine, which, especially the red, incorporates natural colouring agents of assistance to the body in assimilating and eliminating alcohol.

What is more, the fact that it is drunk with food makes it physiologically more beneficial.

There are, however, conditions where wine is not recommended or is positively harmful:

1. Inflammation, irritation or ulceration of the mouth, gullet, oesophagus or stomach, and also, as with other alcoholic drinks, cases of gastritis, gastric hyperchlorhydria, stomach ulcers and cancer of the stomach. Nevertheless, wine (red for preference) can help in curing many duodenal ulcers.

2. Wine is clearly contra-indicated in cases of pancreatitis, and should be used with the utmost care when there are any symptoms of disease of the liver.

3. Kidney infection.

4. Wine and all alcoholic drinks are contra-indicated in all cases of prostitis or genito-urinary troubles.

5. It should be taken with great care, or not at all, by epileptics.

6. Alcohol of any type may produce secondary reactions when taken in combination with barbiturates, tranquillizers, narcotics or similar drugs. When prescribing them, doctors should be careful to supervise and control the consumption of wine.

Wine as Nourishment

There are 80 calories per 100 ml of table wine, and it is an excellent source of energy easily assimilated by the body. The calories obtained from wine are used by the body for general maintenance and muscular energy, but studies have shown that their contribution to human nourishment should not exceed 40 per cent of the total intake.

The effect of wine on human longevity is not known, but statistical studies suggest that moderate drinkers live longest, with abstainers coming next, and finally those who drink to excess.

Vitamins and Minerals

Wine contains various vitamins and, although present in moderate amount, they make a significant contribution to the daily requirement of the body.

Wine as food.

Vitamin C is found in fresh must and during its fermentation, but disappears later; it is, however a common and authorized practice to add Vitamin C (ascorbic acid) to wine shortly before bottling, as this helps to preserve it.

Vitamin A is present only in minute quantities; but wine contains several vitamins of the B group: biotin, choline, cyanocobalamine, folic acid, inositol, nictotinic acid, pantothenic acid, para-aminobenzoic acid, pyridoxine, riboflavin and thiamin. Recent authors have suggested that in the colouring matter of red wines (anthocyanins and tannins) there may exist a Factor P, which, in certain circumstances can replace Vitamin C in physiological processes. In addition, this Factor P may well promote elasticity of the arteries and even exert a moderating effect on cholesterol.

Small quantities of iron are found in wine, and for this reason it is specially indicated in cases of anaemia.

Wine and the Appetite

It is an accepted fact in modern medicine that eating too little or too much can result from anxiety or emotional stress; and, although these symptoms are opposed, the tranquillising effect of wine can be of therapeutic value.

Wine in the kitchen ('The Bakery' restaurant in Chicago).

In cases of anorexia (loss of appetite) a dose of 100 ml of wine, taken once or twice a day at mealtimes, may prove beneficial. For those suffering from obesity, and especially when over-eating is a consequence of emotional distress, wine can also be of great help. It is easy to prescribe a diet for losing weight, but often difficult to adhere to it, and it has been shown that appropriate use of wine can play a part in an anti-obesity programme, because it makes it easier for the patient to adapt to the recommended diet. It is suggested that from 100 to 200 ml of dry red table wine should be drunk about half-hour before food or with the main meal of the day. Research undertaken in America and Italy has shown that when wine is included in an anti-obesity diet, most patients tend to lose their desire for carbohydrates.

Taking wine before going to bed can alleviate insomnia, so removing the temptation to indulge in 'snacks in the small hours', to which insomniacs are so prone.

Wine and the Stomach

The acidity of wine (pH value) is nearer that of the gastric juices than is the case with any other natural beverage, and this makes it the drink *par excellence* to take with food. In small quantities it increases the production of saliva, gently stimulates the digestion and assists in the natural evacuation of the bowels.

By relaxing and tranquillizing the invalid without causing local irritation, small amounts of wine can be of benefit in the treatment of duodenal ulcers; it is a question of individual reaction. Its tannin content and antiseptic properties are also of use in the treatment of intestinal diarrhoea and other infectious diseases affecting the gastro-intestinal system.

The functioning of the pancreas is likewise assisted by the moderate alcohol content of wine, just as strong alcoholic drinks have the opposite effect. This explains why wine helps the digestion of rich and heavy meals.

Cirrhosis of the liver cannot wholly and exclusively be blamed on excessive consumption of alcohol. An alcohol intake of 80 gm a day (equivalent to three-quarters of a litre of wine) does not involve any danger of cirrhosis; there is some risk with amounts of up to 160 gm a day; and above this it is very real. Modern research has incidentally shown that cirrhosis can be caused by malnutrition, especially when the diet is deficient in proteins and vitamins; also by viral and parasitical infections; and even by excessive consumption of sugar and certain soft drinks.

It is of interest that the majority of hospitals and clinics in the United States include moderate amounts of wine in the diet of convalescent and post-operative patients. Additionally, some centres, such as the Bellevue Hospital in New York, the Boston City Hospital, the San Francisco General Hospital, the Los Angeles County Hospital and the Massachusetts General Hospital use wine in the treatment of cirrhosis in conjunction with a diet adequate in proteins and vitamins.

Wine and Emotional Tension

Among all the drinks and foods known to man, none other possesses the gentle stimulating effect of wine. It helps to promote human communication, something more than ever necessary today, when there is such a crying need to revive the lost arts of conversation and of lively and intelligent discussion.

Scientists have analyzed the properties of wine and, using the encephalogram, have investigated its effect on the hypothalmic gland. Rigorously controlled laboratory experiments show that wine relaxes tension in human subjects; but if it is replaced by a solution of alcohol in water, the results are quite different. This appears to be a good argument for moderate indulgence in wine as opposed to strong alcoholic drinks, which can never replace it.

'Wine, the last companion'.

Wine in Old Age and Convalescence

The tranquillizing effect of wine is of particular interest in the treatment of the elderly and of patients recovering from illness.

With old people, its soothing effect may not by itself solve any problems, but at least it helps them ward off disturbing thoughts, forget the ingratitude of children —real or imagined— and to adapt to unfamiliar or uncomfortable surroundings. Of the sedatives used for insomnia, so prevalent in old age, wine has without the shadow of a doubt the most to recommend it, and the types most suitable are

sherry and port. Contrary to popular belief, strong alcoholic drinks create conditions of stress rather than relaxing it. Also, in the case of the elderly, wine is both nourishing, and at the same time stimulates the appetite and aids the digestion.

Convalescents can be helped to take an interest in other people, to escape from undesirable introspection and generally to achieve physical and mental relaxation.

Wine and Diabetes

From the earliest times dry wine has been used in the treatment of diabetes, and although its employment was then purely empirical, it is now known that there is no illness for which wine is more to be recommended or its consumption more justified.

The explanation is simple; with the exception of sugar, wine of all foods is the most easily oxidizable. But, with wine, metabolism takes place without the agency of insulin, and it therefore supplies the diabetic with a ready source of energy. Unlike other alcoholic drinks, it is absorbed relatively slowly by the digestive tract, so resulting in low alcohol concentration in the blood and providing energy at the steady rate required by the body.

A survey of 480 Americans of Italian origin was recently carried

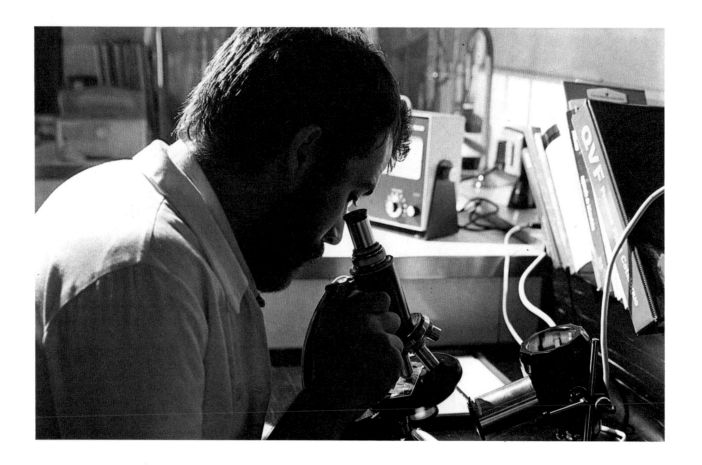

Biological investigation with a microscope.

out in the United States, and it was discovered that 15 were diabetics and 58 border-line cases. Unlike the others most of these 73 patients were not regular wine-drinkers; and it may therefore be concluded that wine has a certain prophylactic action in regard to diabetes.

Wine and Cardio-vascular Complaints

Wine and brandy have been used in treating illnesses of the heart and arteries since the eighteenth century, and modern clinical studies confirm their efficacy. It has been shown that their usefulness depends on other components as well as alcohol. Wine contains therapeutically-active colouring matter (phenolic compounds); and brandy, a substance which dilates the coronary arteries.

Wine is also useful in preventing the onset of cardio-vascular diseases, since it has been proved that the percentage of adults

'The Triumph of Bacchus'
(Velásquez).

suffering from coronary disease is significantly less in European countries, where wine is a normal part of the daily diet, than in others. This has been put down to the effect of wine in reducing absorption of fats and cholesterol.

The first solidly based scientific studies were those of Fay Morgan and her collaborators in the U.S.A., published in 1957. A series of experiments was carried out on rats and hamsters, in which 1 % of cholesterol was substituted for a similar quantity of lipids (fats), so as to investigate the effect of this exogenous cholesterol on the metabolism of the animals. They were finally divided into separate batches according to the drink which they had been given: water, 15 % alcohol, or red wine adjusted to 15 % of alcohol. When the amounts of total lipids in the blood, and of cholesterol in the blood, liver and suprarenal glands were measured, it was found that the lowest were in the animals that had drunk the wine. The conclusion is that wine does not behave simply like a dilute solution of alcohol.

J. Masquelier of Bordeaux later attributed this to the presence of leucocyanidins, the main component of the colouring matter in red wines; and more recent work confirms his results. Evidence has also come to light of the presence in wine of flavenols, related to the more complicated and physiologically more active leucocyanidins. Indirect proof has further been supplied by one of the large German pharmaceutical companies, which has registered a derivative of flavone, very similar to leycocyanidin, for reducing the level of cholesterol.

Arteriosclerosis

Wine affords protection against excessive amounts of exogenous cholesterol, and there is evidence to suggest that its regular use can reduce the incidence of arteriosclerosis by as much as 50 per cent.

Wine and Cancer

In the United States, Cola, Buchalter and Ulubelen, and also Caldwell and Cola have studied the effect of certain plants in reducing tumours, and have succeeded in isolating the active components. They turn out to be derivatives of the same leucocyanidin found in tannin from wine; and if these experiments fulfill their promise, they may well lead to the conclusión, as yet premature, that red wines can be of use preventing cancerous diseases.

Diuresis

It is well-known that white and sparkling wines possess a diuretic effect; red wines, on the other hand, because of their tannin content, are anti-diuretic.

Antibiotic Therapy

Wine is an acknowledged bacteriocide, and it has recently been found that patients undergoing treatment with penicillin or streptomycin may safely drink white wine. White wine is also beneficial in conjunction with aureomycin and terramycin, since it prolongs and heightens their action in the bloodstream.

Wine and Alcoholism

It is unfortunate that in Spain the alcoholic has always been associated with a bottle of wine. In France, where alcoholism is also a problem —the average Frenchaman drinks 103 litres of wine a year as against the Spaniard's 67.1 litres— there have been energetic campaigns to reduce its consumption. Paradoxically, in Italy, where there is an even higher consumption of 110.1 litres annually, alcoholism is virtually unknown. Its high incidence in France perhaps relates to the drinking of large quantities of strong spirits, such as Calvados and fruit liqueurs, especially in the north.

Far from being an alcoholic, the Latin is usually a moderate drinker of wine; and it should be remembered that, for many alcoholics, alcohol is an easy means of escape from hostile surroundings and a way of avoiding problems (whisky, as they say in Scotland, is the quickest way out of Glasgow —J.R.). The Latin is open and communicative and does not normally stand in need of such recourse, quickly entering into conversation and having no inhibitions about discussing his problems —even those of the most intimate nature.

The wine-lover does not drink in search of escape or artificial euphoria, or to become drunk; wine has always been, and is still today, a traditional bond of union which helps people to

Alcoholism: a real social problem.

communicate. It is normally drunk with food, so that the alcohol is absorbed into the bloodstream slowly and in moderate quantity. Wine is man's companion. It invigorates him, lends strength to his body and agility to his mind, besides stimulating conversation, raising his spirits and making him healthily happy.

Conclusion

The use of wine in medicine is every day becoming more generally accepted. Unfortunately many Spanish doctors tend to recommend to their patients, especially the better-heeled, drinks with high alcohol content —and what is more, foreign ones—, relying on snob appeal and perhaps thinking that they are flattering to the ego. On the other hand, in countries such as England, the U.S.A. and Canada, where there is a tradition of drinking strong liquor, doctors are unanimous in their praise of wine; not only do they recommend it to their patients, but drink it themselves, many of them becoming real connoisseurs.

Many of the experiments and studies to which I have referred are taken from a book published by the Wine Advisory Board of San Francisco, published in 1975, and it is available to doctors who may wish to go more deeply into technical details beyond the scope of the present book. And at this point I should perhaps explain why most of the books listed in the bibliography are by foreign authors and doctors; the truth is that since the time of the celebrated Dr. Gregorio Marañón, very little has been written in Spain in praise of wine.

Dr. Gregorio Marañon, celebrated for his writings on wine.

CHAPTER IX

Wine and the consumer

Once wine has been made, matured and bottled, it reaches the consumer through the normal commercial channels. According to his taste and pocket, he has a wide choice of different types of wine in Spain, since it is a country which produces them in great variety. Wines of the highest quality are obtainable in every bracket, but even today one comes across wines which have been badly made, have been adulterated, or smell and taste unpleasant. How is this possible?

Natural Wine

No drink known to man has a better right to be called natural, since it is the fermented juice of the grape and can be made in such a way that it reaches the customer absolutely pure and without the addition of foreign matter. Nevertheless, there is an idea abroad that there are 'chemical' or 'artificial' wines. Do such wines really exist?

It is still completely impossible to manufacture a synthetic wine, though, of course, it is feasible to make up a solution of water with the appropriate amount of alcohol and to add to it organic acids (tartaric, malic and citric), similar to those of wine, and artificial colouring matter. Finally an attempt can be made to imitate a bouquet by recourse to synthetic scents; but the result cannot compare with real wine.

There have been times of scarcity, as a result of wars or ruined harvests, when natural wine has been mixed with a fraudulent imitation to make something for day-to-day consumption. Examples of such dishonest practices have come to light in Italy and France, but never in Spain. Can it be that there is no dishonesty in the Spanish wine industry? The real reason is much simpler: in Spain, ordinary wine has been —and still is— scandalously cheap, and in 1979 a litre of *vino corriente* from La Mancha cost only fourteen pesetas (roughly 8p or 15 cents). An artificial mixture would be more expensive, and in any case the *Servicio de Defensa contra Fraudes* (Department for the Prevention of Fraud) of the Spanish Ministry of Agriculture is constantly on the watch. From time to time, and without prior notice, it takes samples of bottled wine from shops and also carries out comprehensive inspections of the *bodegas* where the wines have been made and matured. Modern analytical methods are very precise, and dishonesty is easily exposed.

Wine is a Man-made Product

To the extent that wine originates from the fermentation of grape juice, wine-making is a natural process, but the biological development of a wine does not end there; it has a tendency to turn into vinegar, and only the timely intervention of the cellarman and oenologist can prevent this.

It is of interest to examine the extent of this intervention as authorized by the *Estatuto de la Viña, del Vino y de los Alcoholes* (the government code), which is broadly similar in its provisions to the laws of France, Italy and other countries.

1. Corrective Practices

The grape juice must be 'corrected' before fermentation, since, for example, the must will be low in acid in excessively hot years. Moderate additions (between 1 and 3 gm/litre) of tartaric or citric acid —both naturally present in wine— are then permitted, with the object of ensuring the correct sugar-acid balance, essential if the wine is to be healthy and well-made.[1]

On the other hand, in cold and wet years, when the must is lacking in sugar and would produce a weak wine of low alcoholic strength, the addition of concentrated must from the same grape is permitted. In Burgundy, Bordeaux and Germany —among many other regions— sweetening is carried out by adding cane sugar (white sugar or saccharose), a normal constituent of the diet, and this is known as Chaptalization (see page 74). The alcohol content may not normally be increased by more than 1° to 2°, depending on the year.

It is therefore apparent that the sole aim of these corrective

---

[1] In cold districts it is common practice to neutralize excessive acidity of the must by adding calcium carbonate, later precipitated as tartrate etc.

procedures is to restore to the must natural elements not present in their normal proportions because of adverse weather conditions.

2. Clarifying Agents

These, as has already been explained (p. 64), are used to ensure the transparency and brilliance of the wine. Oenologists have known for a very long time that if whites of egg are added to the wine, they precipitate the solid matter causing cloudiness, and until quite recently the practice was general in many wine-making areas. It is nevertheless inconvenient, since the addition of the whipped whites to the wine is both tricky and expensive, and it is also a problem to find a use for the large quantity of yolks that remain.

More common today is the use of gelatine, like that used for confectionary, and isinglass; and in Spain these clarifying agents are made solely in laboratories under the supervision of the Ministry of Agriculture. Some hours after their addition to the wine they are deposited on the bottom of the container, and the clarified wine is usually racked the following day and then filtered through cellulose sheets so that no particles of the clarifying agent are left.

3. Additaments to Wine

Oenology is now-a-days a preventive and not a curative science, and the sophisticated modern laboratories concern themselves with the analysis and composition of the wine. They find out whether its natural components are in balance; whether it is capable of resisting attacks from bacteria (analogous to those that cause human sickness); and also whether it will benefit from ageing —some wines from poor harvests do not— and, if so, for how many years.

The practice of burning sulphur inside containers and casks, so as to sterilize them and prevent contamination of the wine (see page 58), has been sanctioned for thousands of years. The mediaeval cellarman simply followed tradition, but today it is known that the gas derived from burning sulphur (sulphur dioxide) is a powerful germicide; the ancient custom still continues, and one often notices the characteristic smell when visiting *bodegas* and *cavas*.

Not unnaturally, when the wine is later poured into the container, small quantities of sulphur dioxide gas are absorbed, but the total amount allowed by law never exceeds 0.350 gm/litre and is perfectly innocuous and of no harm whatsoever to the human body. With the scrupulous hygiene of a modern *bodega,* the amount of sulphur dioxide can be reduced to 0.100 gm/litre —and even less in the case of some red wines. Over a period of fifty years, exhaustive

*The measuring-cylinders contain
(*Left to Right*): unclarified wine;
the same wine after addition of
isinglass; and the clarified wine 24
hours later.*

experiments conducted to determine the tolerance of the human body to sulphur dioxide have shown that the maximum amounts allowed in wine are completely harmless; it should also be borne in mind that sulphur, in combined form, is found in human tissues and has a part to play in the complicated biological processes of the body.

A well-made wine requires no other treatment, though it is sometimes advisable to add Vitamin C to prevent oxidation. Modern oenology is progressively more concerned with physical treatments of wine which are above suspicion, and in well-equipped *bodegas,* centrifuges and ultra-filtration plants are now common.

Fraud in Making Wine

As in all food industries there is fraud in making wine. Despite the strict controls of the Ministry of Agriculture, some unscrupulous *bodegas* add preservatives to their wines, and until a few years ago they were sometimes watered. Although not actually harmful, addition of water amounts to adulteration, and it is now-a-days obligatory to state the alcoholic strength on the bottles or other containers in which it is sold. Officers of the Ministry of Agriculture carry out periodic tests to verify the truth of such statements.

The simplest precaution and the best guarantee for the consumer is to buy bottled wine; whether it is a popular wine in a litre bottle or an old vintage from a famous *bodega,* the label is his unquestionable guarantee. The maker is vouching for the product and staking his reputation on each bottle, and if the wine tastes bad or is otherwise suspect, the matter can be reported to the local headquarters of the Ministry of Agriculture (or returned to the vendor, if it has been bought outside Spain).

Although much wine sold from the barrel is honest and well-made, the very fact that it is in an unsealed container makes it difficult to discover who is responsible for any defect. As it passes from the cooperative or *bodega* which made it, through the wholesaler or shipper, and finally to the retailer, responsibility becomes diffused, and it is very difficult to find out where along the line any fraud took place.

In Spain, a bottler, however modest, is obliged by law to maintain a laboratory and to employ an oenologist. He is therefore responsible for the wine he buys, and if he discovers any fault is under an obligation to reject and report it. He is also required to seal all bottles, so as to ensure that the wine reaches the customer in proper condition.

Tasting the new vintage.

Home-made Wine

In former days the visitor to any Catalan *masia* (or farm) was proudly offered *la bota del racó* (the house reserve), and while glasses were generously filled, he was assured that the wine was 'the purest and most natural' to be found. I do not want to disillusion the recipients of this charming hospitality, but I have suffered such unfortunate experiences with home-made wines that I must put matters in perspective.

Since when has the owner of a little vineyard —or an amateur under the guise of a hobby— been able to make wine? It is, of course true that Noah was able to do so thousands of years ago... To begin with, our aspirant will be limited to carrying out a few simple operations handed down by his parents and grandparents:

— To crush such grapes as are in reasonably good state in a 'continuous' press (which can never produce good wine).

— To hope that the must will ferment spontaneously and uncontrolled.

— To rack the wine after fermentation, and

— To 'fix' the wine, that is to say, add something which will make it biologically stable. Sometimes this will consist of an overdose of sulphur dioxide, and at others the addition of a substance of unknown composition, which, he has been assured, will destroy any yeasts or bacteria. Unfortunately, with the exception of sulphur dioxide, these products, such as salicylic acid and bromoacetic acid, are harmful to health and expressly forbidden by the Department for the Prevention of Fraud.

In this hypothetical case of an inexpert, but perfectly honest wine-maker —and such cases do exist— the wine, unless high in alcohol, like sherry or Priorato, will become vinegary or rancid when stored in a barrel or earthenware jar. Alternatively, as very often happens, it will keep for a long time, but cannot be considered a table wine, since it becomes maderized and can be drunk only as an apéritif or dessert wine.

In spite of this, I do know some small growers who make very acceptable wines; and in districts with a long tradition of bottling wine, such as Bordeaux and Burgundy, the small growers bottle them with great success after maturation in oak. Many of them have taken practical courses in oenology or are advised by local experts; as a general rule, a knowledge of oenology is essential to guarantee consistent quality.

Hand-bottling in a peasant cellar.

The Cooperatives

The need to vinify the fruit of their vineyards correctly, year in and year out, has induced viticulturalists to group themselves into cooperatives.

In this way they have access to modern machinery adequate to their needs; but the sales side has proved more difficult, and in general the cooperatives limit themselves to supplying wine in bulk to merchants or the owners of large *bodegas.*

The Denominación de Origen (D.O.)

Just as in France many districts were demarcated in the nineteenth century and protected by an *Appellation Controlée,* so in Spain today numerous regions possess their *Denominación de Origen.* How important is this to the consumer?

The D.O. is an agreement entered into by all the parties involved with the vineyards and wines of a particular district, aimed at perfecting quality and raising the prestige of their wines. It calls for the collaboration of growers, makers, maturers and blenders of wine, and finally the brokers and shippers. All accept a series of restrictive measures designed to limit production, control quality, and ensure the consumer a guaranteed product.

As an example, I quote some of the restrictions and obligations presently applying to wines qualifying for the *Denominación de Origen Penedès* (Barcelona). These regulations, recently amended and upgraded, are today the strictest of the D.Os. relating to table wines.

A. Relating to Vineyards

Wines qualifying for the D.O. must be made only from the approved grapes, producing the best quality. These are: the Xarel-lo, Parellada and Macabeo for white wines; and the Ojo de Liebre, Samsó, Cariñena, Monastrell and Garnacha for the *rosados* and reds.

— Upkeep of the vineyards and pruning of the vines are carefully regulated, and the yield is limited to 55 hectolitres per hectare for red wines and 65 hectolitres for white.
— The grapes cannot be harvested until the *Consejo Regulador* decides that they are fully mature, and in certain circumstances it can refuse a D.O. when the vineyards have been affected by hailstorms, diseases etc., which lower the quality of the wine.

B. Relating to Manufacture

— The use of presses of the 'continuous' type is forbidden, since it is considered that they are unsuitable for fine wines.
— The temperature, cleanliness and sterility of the cellars are controlled.
— Minimum alcoholic strength and other analytical characteristics are laid down for demarcated wines.

C. Relating to Maturation

— A minimum period of nine months is required for white wines, and eighteen months for red.
— There are safeguards to ensure that the year of vintage is correctly stated on the label. (This is to end the abuse of printing imaginary vintages on the label; 1928 was a year that seemed to last for ever.)
— It is obligatory for the wine to be bottled in the district where it is produced. Penedès is the only demarcated region to adopt such strict measures, which guarantee the purity of the product and afford maximum protection to customers both in Spain and abroad.
— Each bottle must bear a number or code, enabling the *Consejo Regulador* to check the products of individual growers. Any breach of regulations is punished by sanctions, extending in the final resort to confiscation of the output and closure of the *bodega*.

The Instituto Nacional de las Denominaciones de Origen

I.N.D.O. is the department of the Spanish Ministry of Agriculture which exercises overall control over the different demarcated zones. Although it sets standards and lays down broadly similar rules for all the *Denominaciones de Origen,* it delegates considerable powers to the local *Consejos Reguladores* or regulating bodies.

The Department for the Prevention of Fraud

This is also an agency of the Spanish Ministry of Agriculture and, as already mentioned, it is concerned with correct procedures for making, maturing and selling wine. Whenever wine is transported in bulk, this Department issues the required licenses or permits, stating the origin, type, alcoholic strength and destination of the wine; and every *bodega* must keep a ledger, inspected at regular intervals, entering into it details of purchases and despatches.

The blending of wines from different regions is permitted, except in the case of wines with a *Denominación de Origen.* This practice, known as *coupage,* is widely employed in the production of 'typed' wines for everyday consumption.

Evaluation of Quality

Quality is evaluated by tasting. With long experience the expert develops a 'taste memory' and can distinguish the region, the approximate age, and the individual maker of a bottled wine.

It should be said immediately that a high degree of alcohol does not denote quality, and wine is not better for being strong, although there is a minimum degree of alcohol below which it is declared unfit for consumption. In Spain, this minimum is 9° (i.e. 9 % by volume); in the Penedès, most white wines vary between 10° and 12°, and the reds between 11° and 13.5°. Normally, red wines of more than 14° are not suitable for drinking with food and are then considered to be apéritif or dessert wines, e.g. sherry, Tarragona clássico, Priorato and Málaga.

Façade principale de la Maison Calvet à Beaune (Côte-d'Or)

Ⓐ PRINCIAL

Ⓑ APPELLATION COTE DE BEAUNE-VILLAGES CONTROLÉE

Ⓐ Trademark

Ⓑ Appellation Controlée

Ⓒ Wine-maker-Shipper
Ⓓ Location of firm
Ⓔ Domaine-bottled

Ⓒ J. CALVET & Cⁱᵉ, NÉGOCIANTS  ÉLEVEURS A BEAUNE (CÔTE-D'OR) Ⓓ

PRODUCE OF FRANCE  Ⓔ MIS EN BOUTEILLES DANS NOS CAVES   JOUFFROY & Cⁱᵉ BEA NE

122

Ⓐ Wine-maker-Shipper

Ⓑ Year of vintage

Ⓒ Brand name of wine
Ⓓ Denominación de Origen
Ⓔ Alcoholic strength
Ⓕ Location of the bodega
Ⓖ Registered name of the bodega
Ⓗ Contents in cl (centilitres)

Ⓐ Wine-maker-Shipper

Ⓑ Year of vintage

Ⓒ Registered brand
Ⓓ Official control number

Ⓔ Zone of production
Ⓕ Classification of the wine
Ⓖ Alcoholic strength
Ⓗ Contents (in pints and fluid ounces)
Ⓘ Location of the firm

How to Read a Label

There are a number of set rules about the information appearing on a wine label, though the legislation varies somewhat from country to country. Typical examples of labels from France, Germany and Spain are reproduced opposite.

In general it is safest to buy bottled wine, provided that you are able to evaluate the information on the label. Reject any bottle that has been on the shelf for a long time, as evidenced by dust or a discoloured label, or one that has been in a shop window —since sunlight affects wine within a few weeks.

Follow the advice of an informed head-waiter or *sommelier* and above all remember, that wine comprises a whole world of colours and aromas. One should educate one's palate, acquiring a familiarity with different styles and years; and at the same time always be on the look out for new types. Take delight in something that is different —an intringuing colour or a new bouquet— since with wine, as with good cooking, to enjoy it to the full one must always be prepared to experiment.

CHAPTER X

Tasting

To taste is to read a book slowly, phrase by phrase, to capture its full meaning; to taste is to listen to a concert in all its profundity; to taste is to look at a work of art, a picture, sculpture or monument, responding to its forms and colours; to taste is to open one's eyes to a breathtaking view; to taste is to lie on a beach and to feel the sun on one's body; to taste is to be open to every sensation, to be master of oneself and the universe. In short, to know how to taste is to know how to live.

Pierre Poupon, *Nouvelles pensées d'un dégustateur*

The Practice of Tasting

Tasting remains the decisive factor in classifying wines; as my Professor of Oenology at the University of Burgundy used to say: 'The analysis of a wine is like a black and white photograph, but we lack the colours.'

Professional tasting is always done 'blind', with the bottles covered, so that the taster is not influenced by the label, and it always takes place before lunch, between 11 and 1 o'clock, since it helps to have a certain feeling of appetite. It goes without saying that one should not smoke or drink coffee for two hours beforehand, and it is important not to use colognes, aftershave, or any perfume that might affect the other tasters. There can be no compromise about this: scents pose serious problems, and a perfumed hand not only taints the glass, but also interferes with the sense of smell of tasters near-by. Eating cheese at such sessions is not to be recommended, since it inevitably leads to overvaluation of the wine that follows; and all that is needed to refesh the palate is to rinse out the mouth with a little water, which should not be too cold, or to chew a little plain bread.

Tasting demands concentrated effort, and one should at least close the eyes while comparing the sensations produced by a wine with others stored in the 'taste memory'. Each taster should note down his personal impressions, putting them into terms that he can later discuss with his colleagues at the tasting.

The Physiology of Tasting

Various senses play their part in tasting:

A. Sight

It is important to assess the clarity and transparency of the wine and also to note whether or not it gives off bubbles of carbon dioxide. Rotation of the contents gives an idea of their density; and one should observe whether there are 'legs' clinging to the sides of the glass, as happens with wines rich in alcohol.

The colour is also important; for example, yellowish tones in a white wine suggest that it will probably have a maderized nose and that it has lost its freshness. With the reds, a purplish red with violet overtones indicates that the wine is young, while a brick-red colour is unmistakable evidence of a wine that is already two or three years old.

B. Smell

This is the key to all wine-tasting and, to the experienced taster, affords extensive information about the wine.

First, the wine is smelt without moving the glass, and then it is rapidly rotated, so that its aromas can be savoured to the full. These scents are normally of eight types:

1. Floral (reminiscent of particular flowers).
2. Woody (smelling, for example, of oak).
3. 'Green' (as with wines that are acid or bitter).
4. Resinous (resembling smell of cedar and fir trees, and sometimes an indication of faulty maturation).
5. Fruity (evocative of certain fruits).

6. Animal (the smell of some wines is reminiscent of game, leather or damp hair).
7. Musty (normally disagreeable, smelling, for example, of mould. 'Corked' wines come under this heading).
8. Spicy (smelling of cinnamon, cloves etc.)

There is also a second classification relating to the process of making the wine:

1. The 'primary aroma', stemming from the grape used in making the wine. This can be entirely characteristic: for example, the wines from the Cariñena vine always smell of violets.
2. The 'secondary aroma', arising from fermentation; a badly made wine can acquire a 'herbaceous' odour.
3. There is finally the true bouquet, which originates exclusively during maturation, either in oak or later in bottle.

There follows a little 'dictionary' of words often used to describe the bouquet of a wine; and it is helpful to memorize some of them, at the same time recalling the sensations which they produce on your sense of smell.

lime blossom	hazel nut	cinnamon
crushed vine leaves	vine flowers	cumin
apple	rose	aniseed
peach	violet	truffle
plum	magnolia	vanilla
black currant	honey	bitter almond
strawberry	tobacco	burnt caramel
raspberry	hay	toast
cherry	cloves	green coffee beans
banana		liquorice

C. Taste

Contrary to what is often thought, the tongue does not have a tasting function; its fundamental purpose is to warm the liquid so that aromas are released and so activate the taste centre. The 'chewing' of liquid in the mouth causes the vapours to ascend to the olfactory bulb, which then sends information through the nervous system to a brain centre devoted to taste, where aromas are distinguished and analyzed. This is why it is so important to hold the wine on the palate for a few moments, to help warm it and develop the scent. All professional tasters make use of this practice of chewing, known in Spain as *barboteo,* which consists in taking a small quantity of wine into the mouth, slightly opening the lips and drawing air over the wine, and then expelling it through the nose. But a word of warning —first practise repeatedly with water until you have mastered the art.

The tongue by itself registers five specific sensations: acid, sweet, salt, bitter and harsh. It contains approximately three thousand taste buds, all connected to the brain by the nervous system, and is divided into specialized zones for detecting these different sensations. For example, the edges of the tongue are particularly sensitive to an acid wine or lemonade, and one has a sensation of tasting them precisely in that area. The sensation of harshness is felt when the tongue is rubbed against the roof of the mouth; if the wine is harsh and tannic, it 'sticks' on the palate.

The following words are commonly used to describe different types of taste:

A professional wine-tasting.

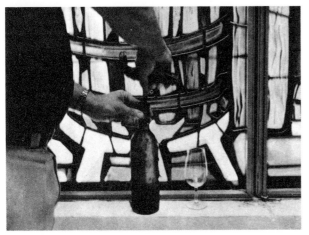

Juan Font Guasch, champion wine-taster of Spain, at work.

harsh	fresh	well-balanced
hard	robust	velvety
nervous	delicate	silky
coarse	full-bodied	luscious
fine	round	

Sometimes these attributes can be expressed in terms of opposites: for instance, the reverse of a wine of character would be a thin or weak wine.

Whereas the eye and ear respond to a definite frequency, the sense of smell can register an unlimited variety of sensations and can therefore be considered the most subtle; over the years an experienced taster acquires millions of different impressions.

After-taste

'Noble', well-made wines are characterized by leaving a 'memory' on the palate after they have been drunk, and the sensation lasts for some seconds. In France, and sometimes in Spain, this phenomenon is called *arrière-gout,* and in England, 'after-taste' or 'finish'.

Defects in Wine

Lastly, there follows a list of terms used to describe defective wines:

— Syrupy (wines with an aroma of boiled must)
— Maderized or oxidized (reminiscent of the scent of a Manzanilla sherry or Madeira. It is considered a fault in white or rosé wine).
— Tart
— Tannic
— Thin
— Spent (i.e. decrepit or too old).
— Artificial (relating to smell and flavour).
— Metallic (resulting, for example, from badly washed pipes)
— Vinegary or sour (when the smell is reminiscent of acetic acid or vinegar). This term is not, however, applicable to wines evolving small bubbles of carbon dioxide, or when the wine is naturally acid. In this case it is described as 'green', astringent, hard or just 'acid'.
— Musty. Corks often enough smell musty, but one should not blame the wine, since it is more or less impossible to detect a defective cork. When necessary, check; and if the cork smells of mildew, ask your supplier to replace the bottle.

Final Considerations

As has been explained, the important things in tasting are concentration and subjective opinion. Just as bridge players sit poker-faced and avoid any word or gesture that might give away their hand, so the taster should shun any word or action that might influence his companions or affect their judgement. Do not show your cards until the end of the game.

The ideal room for tasting should be quiet, well-ventilated and free from extraneous odours; and although it is often thought that cellars are suitable, I believe that their coolness, the presence of the rich aroma of wine and their solemn atmosphere all create conditions prejudicial to forming impartial opinions. Contrary to hallowed belief, a cellar is the last place for a tasting. If a wine is to be judged impartially, it must be taken into the light of day and away from surroundings that might influence the taster; and the bottle must be covered with a cloth so that the label is not visible.

I have been talking about professional tastings; it is a different matter when a bottle is being enjoyed among friends with good food, when all its virtues and its pedigree should be pointed out with pride. But a word of advice —when serving a red vintage wine, be careful not to disturb the coating of dust and mildew on the bottle, the product of so many years. It is the most appropriate mantle for an old wine, and as was said by our ancestors, a good cellar is a harem within reach of us all.

It is not simply physical impressions that one experiences at a tasting; there is a poetry about it, and wine appeals on two levels, intellectual and sensual. Wine speaks to us; it explains its origins in the vineyard, how it was made and how it has slept in the depths of the cellar. Let us learn how to listen.

CHAPTER XI

Wine with food

It was long ago said that 'a meal without wine is a day without sun', and it is difficult to enjoy food without drink, whether it be wine, beer or cider. And let us not criticize the great diversity of other drinks to be found both in Spain and abroad. Many of them go well with food; they are light, nourishing and exhilarating, and at the same time aid the digestion and stimulate the appetite.

Nevertheless, wines, brandies and liqueurs are the ideal accompaniment of a good meal, since more than just liquids, they are, as Pascal said, 'Liquids that think'. They possess a life and body of their own and, for all with the taste to appreciate them, scent and taste... In a word, they are 'individuals' with a living personality, and the true gourmet will learn to elevate his need for food and drink to a fine art.

Wine for Everyday and Special Occasions

In most Spanish homes wine is drunk every day; usually it will be of the previous year's harvest, a young wine that has not been matured or aged, but is often honest and pleasant. Such everyday wine is sold in litre bottles with a plastic cap or crown cork, and it is certainly not expensive. Although in recent years bottling has become the norm'—and do not forget that the label is the maker's guarantee and the customer's safeguard— it is still possible to find acceptable bulk wine sold from the barrel.

It is unfortunate that in Spain quality wines matured for two years or more are subject to 'Luxury Tax' and also a levy for 'Agricultural Social Security' —the latter, in theory, going to the farm worker in case of illness. These impositions add 35 per cent (at 1976 rates) to the original cost and are taxes on quality; but, in its wisdom, the Spanish Government considers that a decent wine comes under the heading of a luxury. Apart from these fiscal burdens, there are other factors which explain the difference in price between a bottle of ordinary wine and a wine of quality:

1. The vines from which the better wines are made are generally of low yield and, in the interests of quality, are cultivated in dry and barren soil.
2. Ordinary wines are usually made in large cement vats, whilst quality wines are fermented in stainless steel vessels or in oak casks at controlled temperatures.
3. Ordinary wine is bottled and sold only three to four months after the harvest, whereas good wines usually spend years, maturing in oak casks in underground cellars.
4. Ageing in bottle, that is to say storing the wine after it is bottled for one or more years, requires so much capital that it is out of the question for ordinary wines.
5. Finally, there are small differences in the quality of the bottle, the label, the capsule and the packaging; and there is a very great difference in the corks, because for maturated wines they must be of the best quality and much longer.

Nevertheless, at the time of writing, it is still possible in Spain to find decent bottles of mature wine in the shops for around 100 pesetas, and it is a consolation to know that it is cheap in comparison with most other countries. There are those living on a modest budget who prefer to drink less and better; a bottle of red wine can be kept for up to two days if it is properly corked, and one may economize in this way.

But it goes without saying that a 'good bottle' is called for on those special occasions when there are flowers on the table and the best linen, cutlery and china are brought down from the shelves. After the hard-worked hostess or the chef in a restaurant has spent time and effort in preparing a beautiful meal, it is then up to the host or *maître d'hôtel* to play his part by seeing that the wines and liqueurs live up to it.

The Choice of Wines

A wine is not chosen solely in regard to the food which it is to accompany; other factors must be taken into account, such as the time of year, the hour, the place and the tastes of the guests. So, a hot summer's day calls for a glass of fresh and lively rosé; in mid-afternoon, among friends, a well-chilled semi-sweet wine is most acceptable; at a beach restaurant, a young and flowery white wine goes ideally with seafood. And on a cold winter's night, in front of a good fire, nothing is more appropriate than a noble old red wine, full-bodied and complex. As it warms slowly in the glasses, giving off its subtle and intringuing aromas, it stimulates discussion and invites comment. It is in company like this that one can pass adequate judgement on a wine —in the manner of a court preparing to do justice.

Gourmets and wine-writers compete with each other in recommending long lists of wines to go with different dishes; and in their opinion one is guilty of a major crime if one disregards the classic rules. In my view, this is entirely wrong, since the purpose of wine is to be enjoyed rather than to weary one with rules and dogmas; and its magic lies in the capacity for giving endless pleasure. Everyone should discover this for himself, disregarding injunctions and taboos.

It was all very well for aristocrats at the beginning of this century

Los Caracoles Restaurant in Barcelona.

to flaunt their knowledge of the precise classification of the *Grands Crus* of Bordeaux, but times have changed, and no longer is a fine wine the preserve of the privileged few. Today Spanish wine is proud to be counted among the great growths of the world, and it has long ceased to be the Cinderella of wines. Every year more interest is being taken in wine and its culture —something so typically Mediterranean and to which the Spanish wine-growing districts have contributed so much. The former prerogative of the few has today become the pleasure of the many who have learnt the art of drinking wine; it is an art which is acquired slowly, but it dignifies all who practise it with dedication, and as Hemingway said:

> Among all the purely sensory pleasures which one can pay for with money, the pleasure of savouring and enjoying wine is perhaps the highest. Knowledge of wine and the education of one's palate are sources of joy throughout life. To taste a wine, learn about it, appreciate and savour it even better until one finally knows it are delights which cannot be bettered.

I myself would not venture to lay down the law about which wines should be drunk with different foods. It is the fashion today to make comparisons with well-known French wines and to talk of 'Chablis-type', 'Burgundy-type', 'Bordeaux-type' and so on. Going to the other extreme, some writers refer to the many demarcated Spanish wines and relate them to different dishes; for example, it is said that with shellfish and other seafood one should drink the white wines of Alella, Valdepeñas, Penedès and the Rioja. It seems to me that this is of little practical help unless one specifies the wines in more detail.

A fresh and fruity rosé is often chosen as a compromise; but Spain is so rich in wines of all types and styles that it pays to learn more about them. Perhaps the people who know them best are those who buy them in the local supermarket or drink them in their favourite restaurants. One should not overlook the smaller wines obtainable only in the districts where they are made. It would be impossible to comment on all of them, but the next chapter describes some of the better-known Spanish wines with *Denominación de Origen*.

Suiting Wine to Food

According to the eminent French writer Charles Quittanson, the first golden rule in gastronomy is never to serve a wine of lower quality than the one which has gone before. The second is to suit the wines to the guests; if they are connoisseurs they should be offered fine wines, for even if the differences are small they will be able to appreciate the subtler overtones. With guests who are not experts, serve wines whose differences they can appreciate at once. The third rule is not to attach too much importance to old vintages; a wine has a limited life and one should periodically taste one's wines and drink those which show signs of old age. A wine that is too old is nothing but a memory, a museum piece.

Dry white wines go well with shellfish and grilled fish, and when slightly sweeter are a good accompaniment to cream sauces. Classical white wines high in alcohol, such as sherry and Madeira, are perfect for drinking with *foie-gras;* and highly perfumed wines can be served with cheese and desserts. Rosé wines can —in theory— be served with anything, or at least as an alternative with any menu that does not include fish: for example, they go with *hors-d'oeuvres,* rice dishes and sweets.

Red wines are reserved for a main meat course, and the best and oldest red wine is traditionally kept for the cheese. It is, incidentally, a hard and fast rule that white wine may be served after a rosé, but never after a red. One may finish off a meal with a sweet dessert wine, such as cream sherry, Málaga and Tarragona; and, most important of all, Champagne may be drunk as an apéritif, but never at the end of a banquet.

CHAPTER XII

The table wines of Spain

by Jan Read

Since wine is so abundant the length and breadth of the country, most Spaniards drink inexpensive *vino corriente* with every meal; and even small children will take a glass of red wine mixed with a little water. The traditional source of supply is the local *bodega* (in its second sense of a 'wine shop'), stone-flagged and redolent of heady, vinous vapours. The casks are lined against the wall, and their contents, mostly of local origin, are tersely described in such terms as *clarete* (red), *tinto* (a heavier red wine), *blanco* (white), *rosado* (rosé) or *vino rancio,* a maderized white wine half way in strength to sherry. Chalked on the casks is the alcoholic strength in degrees and the price in pesetas per litre, and one must bring one's own bottles.

With increasing affluence and the march of tourism, the Spaniards have taken enthusiastically to supermarkets, where the wine is sold in litre bottles, often from cooperatives as far afield as Yecla or Jumilla, south of Alicante; Valdepeñas, in La Mancha; and Cariñena, in Aragón. Until fairly recently the *vinos de marca* or *vinos embotellados (estate-bottled wines),* sold in restaurants and the better-class groceries, were reserved for high days and holidays; but here again there has been a marked change in habits, and there is now a brisk and growing domestic demand for the fine growths of the Rioja and Catalonia. This has been matched by growing exports of fine Spanish table wine, still remarkably good value in comparison with quality wines from most other countries. To Britain alone, shipments of Rioja rose threefold during 1975-1977 and again tripled during 1978, now standing at 235 000 cases a year; the rise in exports from the Penedès has been even more remarkable.

As long ago as 1851 that careful nineteenth-century critic, Cyrus Redding, could write: 'Southward of France geographically, Spain should, from its happier clime as a vinegrowing country, precede it in the excellence of its wines...' and again, 'With every disadvantage in the process of the making, there are both red and white wines in Spain of surpassing excellence. The rude treatment of the grape at the vintage has not made the traveller insensible to this truth.' The somewhat slap-dash methods used in making *vino corriente* were vividly described by another nineteenth-century traveller, Richard Ford:

> Often have we ridden through villages redolent with vinous aroma, and inundated with the blood of the berry, until the very mud was incarnadined; what a busy scene! Donkeys laden with panniers of the ripe fruit, damsels bending under heavy baskets, men with reddened legs and arms, joyous and jovial as satyrs, hurry jostling on to the rude and dirty vat, into which the fruit is thrown indiscriminately, the black-coloured with the white ones, the ripe bunches with the sour, the sound berries with the decayed...

That description might still stand for certain peasant *bodegas* and smaller cooperatives; but the whole recent trend in Spain has been towards the scientific reorganization of the larger cooperatives and the demarcation of favoured districts, where fine wines are produced by the careful methods described in the earlier chapters.

The Geography of Wine in Spain

Very broadly, the country may be divided into three areas:

1. The northern zone, with temperate climate and abundant rain.
2. The drier and sunnier central zone.
3. The southern zone, with the highest temperatures and most sun in all the Peninsula.

Cyrus Redding was of the opinion that the best Spanish wines should come from the sunniest areas; but, although sunlight has never done grapes any harm, excessive heat produces inordinate amounts of sugar in the fruit, yielding coarse table wines overstrong in alcohol. It is therefore in the northern zone, lying below latitude 50° North (see Chapter III), which, for reasons of soil as well as of climate, produces the great Spanish table wines, especially Rioja and Penedès. Because of the excessive rainfall and lack of sun, the north coast produces no wine except for the thin and acid Chacolí from the Basque country; and the characterful 'green' wines of Galicia undergo a secondary malo-lactic fermentation to eliminate acid.

The hotter central zone, embracing the more southerly part of Old Castile, Valencia, La Mancha, Valdepeñas, Alicante, Yecla, Jumilla and the Extremadura, makes a wide range of sound, but less delicate wines for everyday drinking. The extreme heat of southern Spain necessitates special methods of vinification; and Andalusia is the home of the great apéritif and dessert wines, such as sherry, Montilla-Moriles and Málaga, to be described in the next chapter.

The following regions, shown on the accompanying map, have been demarcated and make wines conforming to a *Denominación de Origen:*

Alella	Jumilla	Ribeiro
Alicante	La Mancha	Rioja
Almansa	Málaga	Rueda
Ampurdán-Costa Brava	Manchuela	Tarragona
Campo de Borja	Méntrida	Utiel-Requena
Cariñena	Montilla-Moriles	Valdeorras
Condado de Huelva	Navarra	Valdepeñas
Jerez-Xérez-Sherry and	Penedès	Valencia
Manzanilla-Sanlúcar de	Priorato	Yecla
Barrameda		

Wine map of Spain.

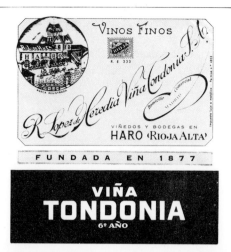

VINOS FINOS

RIOJA
R. E. 333

R. Lopez de Heredia Viña Tondonia, S. A.

Domicilio Comercial
MADRID

VIÑEDOS Y BODEGAS EN
HARO (RIOJA ALTA)

FUNDADA EN 1877

VIÑA
TONDONIA
6º AÑO

H. BEAUMONT Y Cía.
S.R.C.

Nº 0000

Gran vino del
SEÑORIO DE SARRIA

RESERVA 1970

Puente la Reina   Navarra

LA CASA RENÉ BARBIER FUE FUNDADA EN EL AÑO 1880.
DESDE ENTONCES VIENE ELABORANDO VINOS DE MESA DE RECONOCIDA CALIDAD,
CON LOS QUE HA LOGRADO GRAN PRESTIGIO MUNDIAL.

RENÉ BARBIER
Tinto

ELABORADO Y EMBOTELLADO POR RENÉ BARBIER, S. A.
SAN SADURNI DE NOYA (PENEDES)

CONT. 72 CL.   A.I.C. 12'5º

PRODUCE OF SPAIN

12'25º

CALITAX
CONTROL DE CALIDAD

1970

CASTILLO DE
Perelada

VINO DE MESA TINTO
CAVAS DEL AMPURDAN, SA - PERELADA
COSTA BRAVA - PROV. GERONA - ESPAÑA

REGULADOS
RIOJA

REG. EMB. Nº 10-LO.

BODEGAS BILBAINAS

VIÑA POMAL
Bodegas Bilbainas
HARO-RIOJA

EMBOTELLADO EN LA BODEGA

★ RESERVA ESPECIAL ★

1971

Alella Legítimo
de la Bodega Cooperativa Alella Vinícola
fundada en 1906, exclusivamente por cosecheros de Alella
Cataluña 72 cl. Prov. de Barcelona 13º España

GRANDES PREMIOS   En la Exposición Internacional de Barcelona y en el
CON MEDALLA DE ORO Concurso de vinos nacionales celebrado con motivo del
                    II Congreso Internacional de la Viña y del Vino - 1929
Registro embotelladores 616

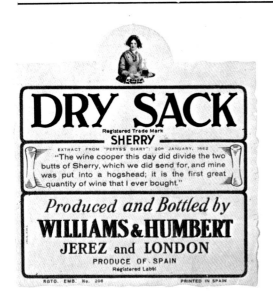

DRY SACK

Registered Trade Mark
SHERRY

EXTRACT FROM "PEPYS'S DIARY"; 20th JANUARY, 1662
"The wine cooper this day did divide the two
butts of Sherry, which we did send for, and mine
was put into a hogshead; it is the first great
quantity of wine that I ever bought."

Produced *and* Bottled *by*
WILLIAMS & HUMBERT
JEREZ and LONDON
PRODUCE OF SPAIN
Registered Label

RGTO. EMB. No. 206   PRINTED IN SPAIN

VINO FINO

VEGA-SICILIA

COSECHA 1959   "UNICO"

Medalla de Oro y Gran Diploma de Honor
Feria de Navidad de Madrid de 1927
Medalla de Oro y Gran Diploma de Honor
Exposición Hotelera de Barcelona de 1927
Gran Premio de Honor
Exposición Internacional de Barcelona 1929-30

Esta cosecha se ha escogido para ser enva-
sada este año y consta de 30.800 botellas.

El número de esta botella es el   Nº   13018

BODEGAS VEGA SICILIA, S. A.
El Presidente

202

CASTILLO DE MACHARNUDO   PROPIEDAD DE DOMECQ

La Ina

REGD. TRADE MARK

JEREZ FINO MUY SECO

SIRVASE FRIO

PRODUCIDO Y EMBOTELLADO POR PEDRO DOMECQ. S.A.
PRODUCTO ESPAÑOL • JEREZ DE LA FRONTERA. ESPAÑA

SHERRY

HEREDEROS DEL
MARQUÉS DE RISCAL
ELCIEGO (ÁLAVA)
1971

R.E.
VI-Nº 308

MARCA CONCEDIDA. MARQUE DÉPOSÉE. TRADE MARK. SCHÜTZ MARKE.

The Rioja

Doffing one's cap in the direction of Catalonia and the Penedès, one may perhaps say that the Riojas are still the best-known of Spanish wines outside the country. They are characterized by their softness, fruitiness and good balance, and above all by their pervading vanilla-like flavour of oak. In fact, the practice of maturing the wines for very long periods in oak has been criticized as old-fashioned —but, of this, more later.

There were already vineyards in the Rioja when the Romans colonized the area —Cenicero, one of the main centres of production, means an 'ashtray' in Spanish and was so-called because the Roman legions cremated and buried their dead near the village. '*Veled Assikia*', as it was called by the Moors, was one of the first regions to be recaptured during the Reconquest, and the redevelopment of the vineyards was thereafter rapid. They supplied wine in large quantity

Red wines from the Rioja, the Penedès and Valladolid.

to the thirsty Conquistadors, and by 1770 a 'Royal Society of Harvesters: had been formed; but it was with the settlement in the region of knowledgeable *vignerons* from Bordeaux during the phylloxera epidemic of the late nineteenth century that the wines were evolved in their present style.

Soil and Climate; the Sub-regions

The district comprises some 43 000 hectares of vineyards extending for about 100 km on either side of the Ebro river, which flows from west to east from the high pass of the Conchas de Haro to Alfaro in the flatter east of the region; Logroño, near the centre, stands at a

Map of the demarcated region of the Penedès.

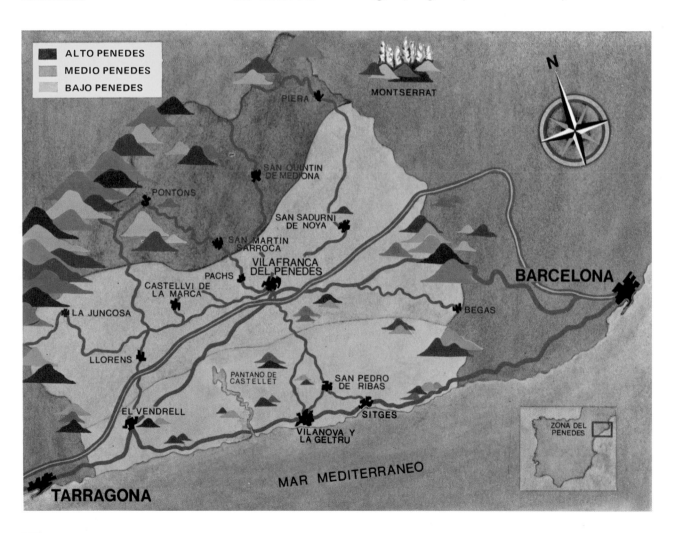

White wines from the Rioja, the Penedès and Galicia.

height of 384 metres. For the purposes of wine production the *Consejo Regulador* divides the Rioja into three sub-regions: the Rioja Alta and Rioja Alavesa to the west, and respectively south and north of the Ebro, and the Rioja Baja to the east. It is the first two which make the best wines; grapes from the hotter and drier Rioja Baja contain less acid and more sugar, and produce coarser, stronger wines, often used for blending and to confer body.

In the favoured west, the Ebro valley is bounded by mountains on either side and is never more than 80 km wide, and the vines grow along the river and on the lower slopes of the hills. The soils are sedimentary; the lower layers contain slates and quartzites, but more important for the vine are the tertiary sandstone, chalk and limestone. The topsoil is an alluvial silt from the Ebro and its tributaries.

Like the soil, the climate is well-suited to viticulture. The winters are not severe; the springs, mild; the summers short and hot; and the autumns, long and warm. The climate is fairly predictable, so that vintage years, though important, are less so than in more northerly regions, such as Bordeaux.

Grape Varieties and Cultivation

Among the many varieties of grape grown in the Rioja, the most important used in making red wines are the Garnacha (akin to the

A vineyard in the Jerez region.

148

Grenache of the Rhône valley), which imparts body and strength to the wine; the Tempranillo, producing wines of 10°-13.5° strength with good acid balance; the Graciano, which confers freshness, flavour and aroma; and the Mazuelo, whose musts are rich in tannin, important for wines that are matured for so long in wood. Different bodegas mix the grapes in varying proportions; a typical blend for a long-lasting wine with full bouquet and flavour might be:

Tempranillo	50 %
Garnacha	25 %
Graciano	15 %
Mazuelo	10 %

Only three white grapes are used in the Rioja, the Malvasía, Viura, and Garnacha blanca.

Cultivation of the vines is along the general lines described in some detail in Chapter IV. They are grown without stakes and wires, *a la castellana,* and pruned *en vaso* (see page 47). Only a few of the *bodegas* grow more 30-40 per cent of their grapes, and the more usual practice is to buy grapes from independent farmers —whose methods and production are, or should be, carefully supervised by the purchasing *bodega.* A less desirable practice, which has sprung up among some of the huge new *bodegas,* is to buy wine ready-made from the cooperatives and simply to blend and mature it; and it is

A vast sherry bodega (Gonzalez Byass).

perhaps a legitimate criticism of the Rioja that more emphasis is sometimes placed on the 'elaboration' of the wine than on viticulture and vinification.

Vinification and Ageing

Apart from a little sparkling *cava,* three main types of wine are made in the Rioja: red (*tinto* and *clarete*), *rosado* (rosé), and white (dry, semi-sweet and sweet). The general methods employed in making these different types of wine have been discussed in Chapters V and VI. The tradition in the Rioja was to use nothing but oak for all the vessels used in making the wines, red, rosé or white; and this is still the case with some of the older bodegas and also at Muga, a firm of fairly recent origin producing wines of the greatest distinction. The new generation of *bodegas,* constructed by interests as diverse as the sherry firms, banks and Basque steel companies, some of them with total capacities of up to 15 000 000 litres, all use stainless steel or cement vats for fermentation, and there is nothing to be said against this.

Most Riojas are to some extent blended, but this is not true of the *reservas,* which are vintage wines grown in especially good years. Whatever its type, red, white or rosé, the *Consejo Regulador* stipulates that a good quality *crianza* wine must be matured for at least two years, one of which must be in 225-litre Bordeaux-type oak *barricas;* the red *reservas,* of course, spend years more in cask. Undoubtedly, the long period in wood gives old Riojas, like tawny ports, a lightness and fragrance. It is a style to which one may soon become addicted, but there is a school of thought which argues that the wines might be even better if they spent less time in wood and longer in bottle —many old *reservas* are bottled very shortly before shipment. Whatever the rights and wrongs of this, white Riojas are apt to lose their freshness through prolonged contact with oak.

It is incidentelly a popular fallacy that Rioja is made by the *solera* system. This is quite untrue; small quantities of wine lost by transpiration from the *barrica* are simply made good with wine of similar type.

The Wines

In the Rioja Alta the bodegas are mostly grouped in and around Haro, Logroño, Ollauri, Fuenmayor and Cenicero; and in the Rioja Alavesa around Elciego, Laguardia and Labastida.

A list of the principal bodegas follows:

La Rioja Alta

AGE, Bodegas Unidas, S.A. (Azpilicueta, Cruz García and Entrena)	Fuenmayor and Navarrete
Bodegas Berberana, S.A.	Ollauri
Bodegas Beronia	Ollauri
Bodegas Bilbainas, S.A.	Haro
Bodegas Campo Viejo	Logroño
Bodegas Carlos Serre, Hijo	Haro
Bodegas Cooperativas Santa María la Real	Nájera
Bodegas Corral	Navarrete
Bodegas Delicia	Ollauri
Bodegas Federico Paternina, Vinos Rioja, S.A.	Ollauri
Bodegas Francisco Viguera	Haro
Bodegas Franco Españolas, S.A.	Logroño
Bodegas Gómez Cruzado, S.A.	Haro
Bodegas La Rioja Alta, S.A.	Haro
Bodegas Lafuente, S.A.	Fuenmayor
Bodegas Lagunilla, S.A.	Cenicero
Bodegas Lan	Fuenmayor
Bodegas López Agos	Fuenmayor
Bodegas Olarra	Logroño
Bodegas Marqués de Cáceres	Cenicero
Bodegas Marqués de Murrieta	Logroño
Bodegas Martínez Lacuesta Hnos., Ltda.	Haro
Bodegas Montecillo, S.A.	Fuenmayor
Bodegas Muga	Haro
Bodegas R. López de Heredia, Viña Tondonia	Haro
Bodegas Ramón Bilbao	Haro
Bodegas Rioja Santiago, S.A.	Haro
Bodegas Riojanas, S.A.	Cenicero
Bodegas Velázquez, S.A.	Cenicero
Bodegas Vista Alegre, S.A.	Haro
Castillo de Cuzcurrita	Rio Tirón
Compañía Vinícola del Norte de España (CUNE)	Haro

La Rioja Alavesa

Bodegas Alavesas, S.A.	Laguardia
Bodegas Cantabria, S.A.	Laguardia
Bodegas Cooperativa Vinícola de Labastida	Labastida
Bodegas Real Divisa	Abalos
Bodegas Faustino Martínez	Oyón

Bodegas Palacio (Seagram Inc.)	Laguardia
Bodegas Pedro Domecq., S.A.	Laguardia
Bodegas Rojas y Cía S.R.O.	Laguardia
Bodegas Viña Salceda	Elciego
Rioja Alavesa S.M.S.	Elciego
Sociedad General de Vinos, S.A.	Elciego
Vinos de los Herederos del Marqués de Riscal, S.A.	Elciego

La Rioja Baja

Bodegas Gurpegui	San Adrián
Bodegas Latorre y Lapuerta	Alfaro
Bodegas Muerza, S.A.	San Adrián
Bodegas Palacios, Vinos Rioja, S.A.	Alfaro
Bodegas Rivero	Arneldo
Savin, S.A.	Aldeanueva de Ebro

Red Riojas

In theory there are two basic types of red Rioja: the *claretes,* sold in Bordeaux-type bottles, are said to resemble the wines from that area in their lightness, dryish flavour, slight acidity and longevity; the *tintos,* which remain longer in contact with the grape skins during fermentation and are sold in Burgundy-type bottles, are considered to be of deeper colour, fuller and softer flavour, and greater body. In practice the style varies so much from bodega to bodega that one firm's *clarete* might be another's *tinto.* Again, the wines from Alava do not always possess the same acidity or finish as the wines from La Rioja Alta —but it would be a bold man who undertook to distinguish between them at a blind tasting.

In the past, Spaniards have considered that the aristocrats among Rioja were the wines from the Marqués de Murrieta and the Marqués de Riscal. The former tend to be fruitier and more fully bodied; and the Murrieta Castillo Ygay 1934, still at its peak, was certainly one of the best wines of the last decades. The Riscal wines are lighter, more nervous and more in the style of claret, and the old reserves can be very fine. Another *bodega* with some very fine old *reservas,* still full of life and body, is Federico Paternina, recently taken over by the great Spanish conglomerate RUMASA.

There are expert tasters abroad who consider that the long years of ageing in oak leaves some of the *reservas* with good initial taste and bouquet and a long aftertaste on the palate, but a little lacking in flavour in between. For this reason they prefer to drink Riojas rather younger.

The difficulty of picking out vintage years, so important in Bordeaux and Burgundy, may be illustrated by the results of a recent blind tasting of some forty red Riojas by an expert panel in London. Among the younger wines most appreciated were:

1970: Viña Ardanza and Viña Arana, La Rioja Alta; Imperial, CUNE; and Viña Zaco, Bodegas Bilbainas.
1971: Viña Vial, Federico Paternina.
1972: Carta de Oro, Bodegas Berberana; Monte Real, Bodegas Riojanas.
1973: Muga, Bodegas Muga; Olarra, Bodegas Olarra; Viña Salceda, Bodegas Salceda; and Rivarey, Bodegas Marqués de Cáceres (a good year —but the 1973 Riscal was not the equal of the 1971).
1974: Viña Cubillo, R. López de Heredia, Viña Tondonia.
1975: Cumbrero, Bodegas Montecillo.

White and Rosé Riojas

Hugh Johnson has written of dry white Rioja that, when drunk young and fresh, it can be 'marvellously stony and up to Rhone white wine standards'. The danger is to mature the white wines too long in oak, when they sometimes become pronouncedly yellow in colour, rather tired and flat, and without much finish. For all this, perhaps the best white to come out of the Rioja in recent years has been the 1971 Viña Tondonia from R. López de Heredia, described recently (spring 1979) by a leading English shipper as 'perfectly dry, beautifully balanced, deep gold in colour and with a long finish in which the oak and the fruit seemed to be in perfect harmony'. Other dry white Riojas to look out for and to drink young are the fresh and aromatic Cumbrero from Bodegas Montecillo, the big-selling Monopole from CUNE, and La Rioja Alta's Metropole Extra. Among the rosés or *rosados,* that from the Marqués de Riscal is an excellent wine, dry and refreshing. There is also a large range of sweet and semi-sweet wines in the white and rosé categories.

The Penedès

Thanks to its soil, climate and geographical position, the Penedès district, a little to the south of Barcelona, makes a larger range of quality wines than any other part of Spain. They include red, white and *rosado* (rosé) table wines; dessert wines such as Sitges and the *rancio* described in the next chapter; a *vino de aguja* with a slight natural sparkle; and, of course, vast amounts of sparkling wine made by the *cava* or Champagne method.

Legend has it that the vine was brought to Catalonia by Gerion, the three-headed giant and enemy of Hercules; be this as it may, it was probably the Greeks who introduced the Malvasía grape used for making the dessert wines of Sitges. Vilafranca del Penedès, the centre of the region, was founded by Hamilcar Barca; and after driving out the Carthaginians during the Second Punic War, the Romans laid firm foundations for the wine industry. The pattern of land tenure, the '*Rabassa Morta*', which has so influenced the production of wine in the region, was established long before James the Conqueror (1213-76) repopulated the agricultural districts after his expulsion of the Moors. The custom was for a proprietor to lease land to a farmer on condition that he planted it with vines, and the agreement expired only after the death of the first-planted vines —a very long period in pre-phylloxera days. Another mediaeval practice was to establish *bodegas* in the hallowed land around churches, where their stocks of wine were free from the attention of thieves.

Several of the large bodegas can trace back their history for centuries: Codorníu, now the largest concern in the world to produce wine by the Champagne method —its *cavas* have been declared a National Monument— was already making still wines in 1551; and the Torres family has owned vineyards since the seventeenth century.

Soil, Climate and Grape Varieties

The Penedès is a limestone area with soils very suitable for viticulture, and the climate is temperate and the rainfall ideal for growing vines. There are three sub-regions.

Bajo Penedès
Medio Penedès
Alto Penedès

The Bajo Penedès, bordering the coast, is wild and rocky and of surprisingly rugged aspect. The climate is hotter than in the other zones, and it is therefore particularly suitable for the cultivation of vines bearing the black Cariñena (not to be confused with the grape of the same name from Aragón), the Garnacha, Ojo de Liebre and Samsó grapes. It has been making great red wines for centuries.

The Medio Penedès is responsible for almost 60 per cent of the wine from the area as a whole, mainly white and made from the

Xarel-lo and Macabeo grapes for use in sparkling wines. The bases for the best sparkling wines are in fact white wines without much personality, but at the same time, light and well-balanced.

The Alto Penedès, rising to a height of some 700 metres in the hills around the Monastery of Montserrat, is almost entirely given over to cultivation of the white Parellada grape. Here the sun shines through the clouds, and the climate is more humid and cooler. It is the zone of the great white table wines, light, delicate and aromatic, and among the best in Spain.

Apart from another native and 'noble' grape, the black Monastrell, a number of foreign grapes have been introduced to the Penedès, where they have been successfully acclimatized and grown in the vineyards of Bodegas Torres. These include the white Gerwürztraminer from Alsace, the Chardonnay from Burgundy and the Riesling from Germany; and the red Pinot Noir from Burgundy and Cabernet-Sauvignon from Bordeaux.

Vituculture in the Penedès has been described in some detail in Chapter IV. It is of special interest that, at Bodegas Torres, the foreign wines are necessarily staked and trained on wires and pruned by the Guyot method —a marked departure in Spain, where the native vines are elsewhere grown low and pruned *en vaso*.

The Wines

Apart from the dozens of *cavas* making sparkling wine, there are numerous well-equipped modern *bodegas* in the Penedès producing table wines of high quality.

Among the most modern are the recently completed Bodegas Bosch-Guell, owned and operated by the Bosch family, whose Clarete fino and Blanco selecto wines have yet to reach the British market. The bodegas of Masia Bach, owned by Codorníu, are situated on a hill looking across to the heights of Montserrat and incorporate several thousand metres of cellars. Extrísimo Bach has long been famous as one of the very best white Spanish dessert wines, lush and fragrant; and the *bodega* also produces the dry white Masia Bach, flowery and refined, and a good red wine. The Marqués de Monistrol is another family firm; its Vin nature blanc de blancs is thoroughly to be recommended, as are the dry Blanco reserva especial and sweet Blanco suave. It also makes a good Tinto reserva and, something of a rarity, a medium sweet red wine, the Tinto abocado, which, when chilled, goes well with oily food.

When all is said and done, the wines which have most gained the Penedès its growing reputation outside Spain are those from Bodegas Torres —and, with all deference to the modesty of our author, Miguel

Torres, I shall describe them at more length.

The scrupulous methods of the *bodega,* both in the culture of the vines and the vinification and maturing of the wines, have emerged in earlier chapters. Most of the grapes are grown in Torres' own vineyards, some 400 ha. located around and spreading up to the hills above. In the past, as in the Rioja, the must was vinified in large oak *cubas* (or vats), some of which survive in the old *bodega,* where they are now used for blending the contents of individual *barricas* before the wine is bottled. Fermentation of all the wine is now carried out in stainless steel tanks. The white wines are not now matured in oak, since it has been found that they emerge lighter and fresher without such treatment. The reds are aged in the traditional oak *barricas* for one to two years; and one of the most impressive sights at the bodega is the eight underground galleries, tunnelled beneath the vineyards and 2 km in length, with a capacity for 20 000 traditional 225-litre *barricas.*

As he has made very plain, it is an article of faith with Miguel Torres that all wines should carry a label stating the year of vintage —and not simply a description such as 4° año, meaning that it was bottled during the fourth year after the harvest— and all Torres wines are therefore labelled according to vintage. There is a large range, both of whites and reds.

The dry Viña Sol and semi-sweet San Valentin, both made from the native Parellada grape, are light and fruity white wines with agreeable bouquet. In addition to the Parellada, the 1976 Gran Viña Sol contains some 20 per cent of the newly-introduced Chardonnay grapes, and since these wines benefit from longer bottle age, they are kept in the *bodega* for some two years before shipment. Fresh, fruity and well-balanced with a long finish and remarkably flowery nose, it is a very good dry white wine. The same characteristics are even more pronounced in the Gran Viña Sol 'Green Label', a wine made in small quantity with similar grapes picked in the most select vineyards of the estates. Newcomers to the range of Torres wines, are the semi-sweet Viña Esmeralda made from Catalan-grown Gewürztraminer and Muscat d'Alsace grapes, and a stylisn Riesling, Waltraud, which have all the Torres characteristics of freshness, fruitiness, and delicate flowery nose. There is also a *rosado,* De Casta, light fresh and crisp, with plenty of fruit.

The youngest of the red wines, the Tres Torres, or Sangre de Toro, made from Garnacha and Cariñena grapes, is full-bodied, deep ruby in colour, with a smooth finish and characteristic fruity aroma. The better wines made from these grapes are given more bottle age —some three to four years for the Gran Sangre de Toro, which emerges as a very big wine with even more pronounced bouquet. The Coronas *reservas* are made from the Monastrell, Ojo de Liebre and Cabernet Sauvignon grapes since 1973 there has been a substantial addition of Cabernet Sauvignon, and they spend rather longer in bottle up to three years for the Gran Coronas five for the Gran Coronas 'Black Label', made, like the Gran Viña Sol 'Green Label', from selected grapes grown in the best vineyards of the estate. They are exceptionally smooth wines with a velvety aftertaste and a bouquet reminiscent of violets. Completely different in character is the beautiful Magdala, the first fruit of the plantings of Pinot Noir grapes, light and dry, with an entirely individual nose.

Other Catalan Wines

Apart from the Tarragona clássico, described among the dessert wines in the next chapter, Tarragona produces large amounts of wine, both red and white, most of it for bulk export and blending. Priorato, which takes its name from the Carthusian monastery of Scala Dei, is a small enclave within the demarcated region of Tarragona. Its best growths are the dessert wines, but it also makes fruity red wines from the Cariñena and Garnacha grapes, high in alcohol, full-bodied and almost black in colour, much used for blending.

Alella, to the north of Barcelona, another area with Roman traditions, is one of the smallest wine-producing regions in Spain. The best of its wines, all of which are matured in oak for one or two years and aged in bottle for another, are made by the large cooperative, which sells them under the trademark of 'Marfil' ('Ivory'). The most popular is a medium dry white with a golden colour and a nose which has been compared with peaches. The Marfil seco, without quite the same roundness, is an excellent dry white wine, crisp and delicate. The cooperative also makes a soft and fruity red, light in colour but with surprising body.

Ampurdán-Costa Brava, near the French border in the Pyrenees, is the most recent of the Spanish regions to be demarcated. Apart from the sparkling wines made by the *cuve close* process at the Castillo de Perelada, it also produces some good reds, robust and full of character.

Navarra

The red wines from Navarra have something in common with those from the Rioja, which it borders to the east, and are sometimes made from the same grapes: the Garnacha, Tempranillo, Graciano and Mazuelo. A name to look out for is the Vinícola Navarra, whose full-bodied and fruity five-year-old Castillo de Tiebas is excellent value.

The best *bodega* in Navarra is that of the Señorio de Sarría, near Puente la Reina and the old pilgrim route from France to Santiago de Compostela. It was constructed by the Huarte family, with interests in building and construction, and was started as a rich man's hobby —but there is nothing amateurish about its model winery with a capacity of 6000 *barricas,* its vineyards which produce all the grapes for the wines, or its coopery which makes the casks from Armagnac oak. The red Ecoyen is matured for two years in oak and then in bottle, and the vintage *reservas,* which are up to Rioja standards, and aged for four years in cask and two in bottle. Its wines are now being exported in growing quantity.

Vega Sicilia

Vega Sicilia, a favourite of Sir Winston Churchill with its cigar box flavour and deep bouquet, is made in a *bodega* on the River Duero, to the east of Valladolid, resembling a small French château. The vineyards, set back somewhat from the river, are on gently sloping chalky land fringed by pine trees; and the wine, all of it red, is made from a mixture of native grapes (including the Garnacho and a little of the white Albillo) and Bordeaux grapes, introduced after the phylloxera epidemic of the nineteenth century and, until recently when new French vines were acquired from Montpellier, still propagated in the *bodega's* nurseries. They are crushed very lightly, and there is no further pressing.

Jesús Anadón, the *bodeguero,* believes in fermenting and maturing his wine very slowly in oak, and no Vega Sicilia is sold less than ten years old, the 'younger' wine being marketed as 'Valbuena'. Vega Sicilia is a wine of which I am personally very fond, but about which one finds mixed opinions; it has, for example, been criticized as possessing too much volatile acidity. A doyen of the London Wine Trade once ventured the opinion that it had been made from the Douro grapes used for port, fermented to completion without being brandied —and this perhaps better than anything conveys an impression of its richness and deep-seated aroma. It is expensive and difficult to find even in Spain, where supplies to the best hotels and restaurants are strictly rationed.

Galicia and the Far North

Along the whole length of the often wet north coast, only one wine is made, the Basque Chacolí. It is an astringent, slightly *pétillant* 'green' wine of only 8° to 9° strength, available in two varieties, red and white, *txakoliñ zuri* and *txakoliñ gorri,* the best coming from around Guernica, Guetaría and Zarauz, and should be drunk young, on the spot and cold. The Vizcainos drink it quickly *—ha de tomarse de golpe.*

You will have difficulty in finding it except in bars, but with the superb shellfish of the Cantabrian coast it can, at its steely best, be pleasant.

Despite its generally wet climate, Galicia in the far north-west produces a vast amount of wine, most of which is consumed locally or by Galician expatriates in Madrid; and to try its wines you will have to go to Galicia itself —no great hardship in early summer, when the mountain slopes, fragrant with eucalyptus and wild thyme, resemble nothing so much as a great rock garden.

Valdeorras, to the east of the region, produces well-balanced, bone-dry, dark red wines and some refreshingly dry whites, now being exported. But these are still wines, and the typical growths from Galicia are slightly *pétillants* and are made in much the same way as the Portuguese *vinhos verdes* by the secondary or malo-lactic fermentation (see page 62) of grapes from high-growing tree-vines. The *rodrigones* or *tutores,* between which the supporting wires are strung, may be hewn from the ever-present granite or made of chestnut —hence the saying: *Quien no tiene madera, no tiene viña* (He who has no wood has no vineyard).

The largest *bodega* in Galicia is the huge Bodega Cooperativa de Ribeiro at Ribadavia, just across the Miño river, which at this point forms the frontier with Portugal. It makes a variety of wines, white, rosé and red, all with a slight sparkle, of which the best is the white 'Pazo' (the word means a seignorial residence), light, dry and with a bouquet reminiscent of Moselle, and made principally from the Treixadura, Godello and Turuntes grapes.

The best Galician wine comes from the regions bordering the Atlantic on the west and is made with the white Albariño grape, akin to the famous Alvarinho from Monçao across the border. Among the choicest wines is the Fefiñanes Palacio made by the Marqués de Figueroa in a tiny *bodega* housed in his splendid palace. Since it is aged in oak for some years, it is a deeper yellow and has less sparkle than most Galician white wine, such as the Albariño del Palacio made by his brother (though not at the palace), which is very pale in colour, extremely dry and somewhat acid, and flowery to a degree. These and other Albariños may be sampled in the Parador at Fefiñanes near Pontevedra or at an annual wine festival held in this pleasant little seaside town during August.

In general, the Galician reds are dry to the point of acidity; and as Raymond Postgate once said of their *compères* from Portugal, 'the first mouthful is a shock'. They should be drunk stone cold.

León

To the south-east of Galicia, but still in the northern half of the
country, the ancient kingdom of León produces both red and white
wines. Its full-bodied red was the favourite tipple of the dons from
Salamanca University; and the *Tierra del Vino* nearer Valladolid has
long been famous for Rueda, a dry, golden *flor*-growing wine of up
to 17° strength with a sherry-like flavour. The Marqués de Riscal is
now making an shipping an agreeable dry white wine (though not in
the same style) made with grapes growing in the Rueda area, and the
Planta de Elaboración y Embotellado de Vinos —somewhat
unfortunately abreviated as 'Vile', but equipped with the most
modern machinery— is producing a range of wines, whose freshness
and delicacy must surprise anyone used to the old, robust *caldos* of
the region. These include an inexpensive and attractive white and
rosé, both light and dry, and the red 'Catedral de León', somewhat
akin to Valdeorras in its astringency. Vile also makes *reservas* with a
hint of oak and a more pronounced aftertaste and bouquet.

Cariñena

Somewhat similar in style to the red wine from Toro is the
demarcated Cariñena from Aragón —'It wasn't I, it was the cursed
Cariñena which got the better of me', wrote the famous Spanish
author Muñoz Seca in an allusion to its strength. It is made rather to
the south of Saragossa and the River Ebro, and production is
dominated by the reds and *rosados,* made from the Bobal, Cariñena,
Juan Ibáñez and Garnacho Negro grapes. The best of the wine is
from private *bodegas,* such as that of the Marqués de Vilallonga, but
the most popular mark in Spain is that of the Cooperativa San
Valero. Not particularly delicate, its red, white and rosé wines in litre
bottles are nevertheless a reliable standby for everyday drinking.

Valdepeñas and La Mancha

In terms of bulk the great plateau of La Mancha, south of Madrid
and the scene of Don Quixote's adventures, is the most prolific of
the Spanish wine-growing areas. This huge region, comprising the
demarcated areas of Méntrida, Mancha, Manchuela and Valdepeñas,
with its seas of vines stretching unbroken to the horizon, supplies
most parts of Spain that do not produce wine themselves. It also
ships vast amounts for blending and export and provides most of the

spirit used for making Spanish brandy and anisette. Most of the often excellent carafe wine drunk in Madrid hails from Valdepeñas, just north of Andalusia.

It is a wine with a long and honourable history. Sancho Panza said of it: 'I drink it when I have the taste and also when they give it to me and I do not, so as not to seem off-hand or bad-mannered'; the Emperor Charles V was so addicted to it that he had it transported across Europe on mule-back during his campaigns in the Low Countries.

The grapes most frequently used for the red wines are the Cencibel, Monastrel and Tintorera; and for the whites, the Lairén. They grow in a subsoil compounded of gravel, chalk and clay; and of this same clay are made the 10ft-high earthenware *tinajas,* in which the wines are traditionally vinified and matured (the newer *bodegas* use cement vats). The wine is drunk young and generally sold during the spring following the vintage; and if it is matured for any further period, this will probably be in the oak *tinas* of one of the great export houses in Valencia or Tarragona, where so much of it is used for blending.

The *claretes* and red *aloques,* made from a blend of black and white grapes, which established the fame of Valdepeñas in the sixteenth century, are dry, deep in colour, contain little acid and from 13° to 15° of alcohol. Considering their strength, one is frequently and pleasantly surprised by their light taste and freshness.

The Levante

The Levante, bordering La Mancha to the east and stretching along the Mediterranean coast from the Ebro delta in the north to Almería in the south, is scarcely less prolific a source of wine for everyday consumption and blending. However, in areas such as Valencia the rich, loamy soil and prolonged summer heat —ideal for the growth of oranges, lemons and vegetables— militate against delicacy in the wines, which tend to be 'earthy' and on the heavy side.

The better wines come from the mountainous hinterland, among them the delicious fresh and fruity *rosados* (rosés) from Utiel-Requena in the hills to the west of Valencia on the rim of the central plateau. Made principally from the black Bobal grape, the *claretes* run to 11° to 12° of alcohol, or as little as 10° in a wet year, and are well-balanced *vinos corrientes,* highly praised by Vicente Blasco Ibáñez —who was an *aficionado* of the wines from his native Levante and wrote a novel entitled *La Bodega* as well as his better-known *Four Horsemen of the Apocalypse.*

There are two demarcated regions in the hills of Murcia, further south: Yecla and Jumilla. Traditionally, the cooperative-made wines from this area were inky black, *poderosos por su densidad* (of powerful density) and contained up to 18° of alcohol, at which point the yeasts were paralysed and further fermentation ceased. Many is the bottle of Yecla which I have drunk in the past and thereupon retired for a long *siesta;* but both wines are now much improved and lighter, thanks to more modern methods of vinification. The dry, faintly flowery white. Yecla is to be recommended, as well as an honest red. These inexpensive wines are now being exported and are excellent value.

The Extremadura

The Extremadura, bordering the western frontier with Portugal, produces seas of undemarcated wine on a commercial scale, and the crowded *bodegas* of Almendralejo are hardly less numerous than those of Valdepeñas. Rather better in quality than the wines from Almendralejo is the sturdy red Medellín from the birthplace of Hernán Cortés, who did so much to introduce the European vine to Mexico. But the best of these Extremaduran wines are made in tiny peasant *bodegas* and are not generally available. Salvatierra de Barros makes a brilliant, intensely-coloured and aromatic red wine, much admired by its *aficionados,* from Garnacha, Almendralejo and Morisca grapes. Cañamero, a *flor*-growing white wine in the style of Rueda may be sampled in the Parador and bars of Guadalupe, the shrine of the Conquistadors; while the big surprise is a peasant-made Montánchez — the only red wins in my experience to grow a *flor.* Orange-coloured, slightly turbid and of 15° strength, it is drunk as a *chiquiteo* before meals in the bars of Mérida — a town that should be visited by anyone interested in Roman remains — and small quantities find their way as far afield as Madrid.

The Islands

The Canary Islands do not make wine of particular interest; and Majorca is, on balance, an importer of wine from the mainland to slake the thirst of its countless visitors. Its *vino corriente* is earthy in the style of the heavier wines from the Levante. However, on his estate at Binisalem, near Inca, José L. Ferrer makes a young and very fresh red 'Auténtico' from the local Montenegro grape; and the *bodega* also makes some excellent, rather spicey *reservas,* which should be tasted on the spot since they are produced in insufficient quantity for export.

CHAPTER XIII

Apéritifs, sparkling wines, brandies and liqueurs

The previous chapters have dealt solely with table wines; but a book on Spanish wines would be incomplete if it did not describe, if only briefly, sherry, dessert wines and other drinks made with a basis of wine.

Sherry

Sunning the grapes on esparto grass mats in the Jerez region.

The very special character of sherry derives from the geography and natural features of the district and also the specialized viticultural and oenological procedures developed during the last few centuries.

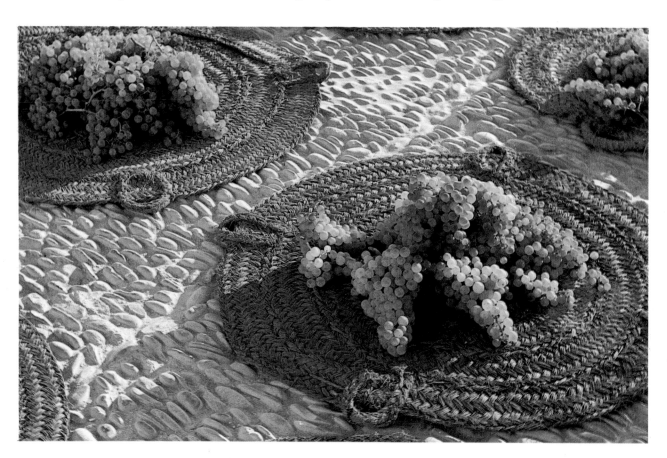

The District

Jerez, which has given its name to sherry, is the largest of the three towns where it is made, the others being Sanlúcar de Barrameda and Puerto de Santa María. Between these places and bounded by the Atlantic Ocean and the Guadalquivir and Guadalete rivers, lie the vineyards, planted in undulating country. The best of the soils is the so-called *albariza,* white and chalky, and extremely light and porous. The proximity of the sea tempers the high temperatures and summer droughts of Andalusia, providing ideal conditions for the growth of the vines and the ripening of the grapes.

Viticulture

Viticulture has reached a high technical level, while still retaining much that is traditional; it is therefore well-adapted to the special conditions of the area and in some respects differs from that of other districts and countries.

Transferage of wine in the solera.

Carrying the sunned grapes to the bodega for fermentation.

The typical vine is the Palomino, also known as the Listan, cultivated in 90 per cent of the vineyards. The Pedro Ximénez and small amounts of other varieties, such as the Muscatel, are grown in the district of Chipiona and are used for making sweet sherry. The Palomino grape ripens well in Jerez yielding musts with a high degree Baumé (a measurement of sugar content) and relatively low acidity. After they have been picked the bunches of grapes were traditionally sunned for a day on esparto grass mats; and for the sweet wines the period is extended to ten or twelve days, when the degree Baumé increases to around 30°.

Fermentation and First Classification

Pressing is carried out in much the same way as for white wines (see Chapter V); and fermentation takes place in *botas jerezanas,* barrels of American oak with a capacity of 500 to 600 litres, only partially filled to allow a space of 50 to 100 litres at the top for air. Once tumultuous fermentation has ended, a film of *flor* ('flower of yeast') immediately appears on the surface of the wine and protects it from further contact with air. This phase lasts until January, when the wine 'falls bright' under its covering of *flor* and is then ready for tasting and first classification. This is the moment when its future is

Maturation of sherry in the solera.

decided. A *capataz* or cellarman can taste up to two hundred *botas* a day and he notes down his conclusions hieroglyphically in the shape of strokes or *rayas* chalked on the bottoms of the butts. The range is from one *raya,* for wine suitable for maturation as a *fino,* to four for wine that can be used only for distillation as brandy.

After classification the wine is racked to separate it from the lees, and the alcohol content is raised to 15° or 15.5°. Once again there is a growth of *flor,* and at this stage, which lasts from one to two years, the wine is said to be *sobretablas.* Wine that is destined for an *oloroso* is fortified to the extent of 18°.

Second and Subsequent Classifications; Maturation

The purpose of the later classifications is to take note of the development of the wine during the phase of *sobretablas* and to define its final style. Different classes of wine are indicated by signs which fundamentally modify the *rayas* assigned to them during the first classification:

√ one or more *palmas* ('palms') for the *finos,* depending on the quality.
φ the stroke used for *olorosos.*

The solera.

† the *palo cortado* ('cut stick') used for *palos cortados,* fresh, full-bodied wines of the *oloroso* type.

‖ rayas, indicating an inferior, full-bodied wine.

Sherry is matured by what is known as the *solera* system, involving a *solera* and several *criaderas.*[1] . A *solera* consists of serried rows of butts, piled high on top of one another, and each of its so-called 'scales' contains wine at a different stage of development. When wine is ready for the market it is drawn off from the bottom and oldest 'scale' comprising the butts on the floor of the *bodega.* A maximum of 20 per cent is removed from each butt and is then replenished from the next 'scale', and so on progressively, the last of the 'scales' being made good with wine from the *criadera,* which is itself replenished with wine in the *sobretablas* stage. This operation is called 'running the scales' and results in complete uniformity of the final product, also an outcome of the remarkably consistent harvests in the Jerez region.

---

[1] The literal meaning of *criadera* is a 'nursery', and like the *solera* proper, it contains rows of barrels where the wine is matured or 'educated'.

There are basically two ways of ageing sherry. A *fino* from Jerez or a *manzanilla* from Sanlúcar de Barrameda is matured biologically in the presence of the *flor,* and the alcoholic strength is kept at 15° to 16 °. The alcohol content of *olorosos,* on the other hand, is raised to about 18°, and this paralyses the yeasts; ageing in this case is therefore a physico-chemical and not a biological process. Other intermediate processes give rise to further types of wine such as *amontillados* and *palos cortados.* There are also the characteristic sweet and cream *olorosos,* blended with sweet wine from the sunned Pedro Ximénez grapes.

Maturation must be carried out in a cool atmosphere with only minimal changes in temperature and humidity, and this explains the impressive architecture of the sherry *bodegas* so much admired by visitors, with the lofty roofs supported by graceful columns and arches and walls of dazzling white. They serve a functional purpose in maturing the wine, and in Spain have aptly been called 'cathedrals of wine'.

Different Types of Sherry

After years of ageing in the *solera,* sherry is a perfectly uniform and characteristic wine, but for commercial purposes and so as to produce the style in most demand, blends called *cabaceos* are usually made by blending two or more types of *solera* wine.

There is a very large range of sherries, and the appropriate moment for drinking them depends very much on national habits and individual taste. *Finos* and dry *olorosos* are best drunk as an apéritif; and in England and Holland, for example, dry sherry before a meal is an established tradition. Sweet *olorosos* and cream sherries go well with sweets or may be drunk after a meal, and whatever the sherry, glasses ought not to be more than half-filled, so that the bouquet can be savoured to the full.

Finos

These are wines with a straw-gold colour and delicate, almond-like bouquet, and are light, dry and slightly acid, with an alcohol content of between 15.5° and 17°. A *fino* sherry is a gay and happy wine, ideal as an apéritif —specially with *tapas,* the savoury appetizers so popular in Spain— and also to drink with fish or shellfish or for use in making *consomés* and sauces. It is best chilled in the refrigerator and served at a temperature of about 10° C.

Manzanillas

Manzanillas are *fino*-type wines, very pale and aromatic, light, dry and slightly acid, and with between 15.5° and 17° of alcohol. Aged in the presence of a *flor* in the *bodegas* of Sanlúcar de Barrameda on the Atlantic coast, they are the lightest of sherries with the tang of their native sea breezes. They are the ideal wines to accompany shellfish and, like *finos* in general, should be served at approximately 10° C.

Amontillados

Amber-coloured wines with a slight pungency like that of hazel nuts, *amontillados* are soft and full on the palate. They are dry, with an alcohol content of 17° to 18° rising to between 22° and 24° as they grow older, and are noble wines to be savoured slowly. They go well with *jamón serrano* (akin to Bayonne or Parma ham) or Manchego cheese and also bring out the flavour of soups.

Olorosos

These wines are old-gold in colour, full-bodied and highly aromatic, with a flavour of walnuts; dry or slightly sweet, their alcohol content is between 18° and 20°. This was the wine that brought fame to Jerez in centuries past and has no equal among sherries, either as an apéritif or for drinking after a meal.

It should be kep in a cool place and served at, or slightly below, room temperature.

Wine tasting at the wine cellars of Terry

Cream Sherries

Cream sherry results from the blending of an *oloroso* with a sweet Pedro Ximénez wine. It is mellow, aromatic and rather sweet and may be drunk at any time between meals, especially in the morning, at teatime or after dinner. It is also delightful when served 'on the rocks'.

Imitation Sherries

Sherry is a unique and exceptional wine, but it has been imitated in other countries, without, I think, much success, since soil, climate and systems of maturation are different.

South Africa, Australia, Cyprus and California all make substutute sherries, with varying degrees of success, and are allowed to use a name which rightly belongs only to wines made in the Province of Cádiz.

It is incomprehensible to me that, while Spanish sparkling wine may not be called Champagne, Californian sherry can be made with impunity in the United States.

Montilla-Moriles

Moriles and Montilla, the two great wines from the Province of Córdoba, are perhaps better-known in Spain than abroad. This is partly because in the past some of their sweet wine from the Pedro Ximénez grape was blended with wine from the Province of Cádiz, and only in recent years have the outstanding growths been fully appreciated.

The principal vine is the Pedro Ximénez, but the grapes are picked at an earlier stage than in Jerez and fermented to completion so that all the sugar is converted to alcohol. The typical sherry-like wine from Montilla-Moriles is therefore a dry *fino,* and because it is naturally high in alcohol, it does not require fortification.

Málaga

Málaga is among the most famous Spanish dessert wines and was once described by André Simon as the perfect 'Ladies' Wine' of Victorian days. Because of the prevailing taste for dry wines, it is not now as fashionable as it once was, and production is on a much reduced scale. The basic grapes are the Pedro Ximénez and Moscatel, and the wines acquire their characteristic bitter-sweet flavour, smoothness and colour, ranging from pale yellow to deep orange, from the blending of old wines and boiled must.

The Generoso[1] Wines of Catalonia

The *generoso* wines of Catalonia are also well-known, though perhaps not as widely as when they were a favourite and inexpensive tipple in the Victorian pubs of England. The type known as Tarragona clássico has an alcoholic strength of 13° to 18° and a sugar content of 2° Baumé[2], and the white and red *mistela*[3] used in making the wines is exported to all parts of the world.

The characterful Catalan *rancio* wine, hardly known abroad, is still made by small farmers in their *masias* and *bodegas,* and these

---

[1] A *generoso* is an apéritif or dessert wine rich in alcohol.

[2] 1° Baumé corresponds to a sugar content of 18 gm/litre, producing 1° of alcohol after fermentation.

[3] *Mistela* is a sweet must, in which fermentation has been arrested by the addition of alcohol.

Spanish sparkling cava *wines.*

maderized dessert wines are also produced by a few commercial firms on a small scale and have a devoted following. They are matured in oak casks and *bombonas* (glass carboys) exposed to the sun and the rain —always a popular sight with visitors. Before the wine is taken to the *campos de añejamiento* ('ageing grounds'), brandy is added to raise its alcohol content to 18° or 19°, as the extremes of light and climate would otherwise rapidly turn it into vinegar. The *rancio* wine is later aged for a further three of four years in oak barrels and blended, according to type, with old *mistelas* to attain the desired sweetness.

The famous Malvasía and Muscatel wines of Sitges —the former site of the Roman city of Subur— deserve a chapter to themselves. Suffice it to say that they are exquisite dessert wines and a local speciality.

Sparkling Wine

Known in France as Champagne, in Germany as *Sekt,* in Italy as *Spumanti* and in Spain as *Cava,* sparkling wine is made all over the world by the method originally discovered by Dom Perignon (see page 21).

The starting point for a high quality sparkling wine is always a still white wine. After the addition of a small amount of sugar and special

The secondary fermentation of sparkling wine (Cavas Codorníu).

yeasts, it is bottled and left in cellars kept at a constant low temperature. A secondary fermentation then takes place with the break-down of the sugar and release of carbon dioxide gas, which gives the wine its sparkle. The next step is to remove the sediment thrown down by the yeasts, and by up-ending the bottles in *pupitres* (or wooden racks) and turning them regularly and carefully over a period of months, it is gradually collected in the necks, close to the corks. A new Spanish invention in the form of large hexagonal metal frames accomodating some 500 bottles enables this process to be carried out with equal efficiency and vastly less labour. Lastly comes the *dégorgement,* or rapid opening of the bottle, when the carbon dioxide gas expels the sediment; the contents are topped up with a little so-called *licor de expedición* and a new cork is inserted, secured by wire as an extra precaution. The result is a bottle of sparkling wine.

Spanish regulations controlling the manufacture of sparkling wines distinguish clearly between three types:

a) *Cava,* made by the Champagne method described above. (The oldest Spanish firms using this method are Codorníu, Freixenet and Segura Viudas).

b) *Gran-vas* or *cuve-close,* in which the secondary fermentation takes place, not in bottles, but in large tanks (*gran-vas*). This is a quicker and cheaper method, but the results are not as good.

c) *Vino gasificado,* made by pumping carbon dioxide into a white
wine and a much inferior product.

In each case the label must specify the type of wine: *cava, granvas*
or *vino gasificado.*

Vermouth and Apéritif Wines

These are made by blending fortified white wine with extracts of
herbs. The darker, sweeter varieties contain sugar or *mistela* in
considerable amounts, and also caramel. In making a dry white
vermouth, only a little sugar and less of the flavouring extract are
added. Various well-known brands of vermouth, such as Martini,
Cinzano and Noilly-Prat are made under licence in Spain.

Brandy

History

It would be unforgivable to write about wine without mentioning
brandy; unlike all other strong alcoholic drinks, brandy is made
exclusively by the distillation of wine and faith fully reflects its
qualities and virtues. In France, brandy was formerly called

A modern distillery in Cognac.

eau-de-vie, and in Spain, *aguardiente* —a word still used to describe spirits distilled from fruits, and of these the grape is the most important.

Was the word 'water' (*agua* in *aguardiente, eau* in *eau-de-vie,* and *wasser* in the German *kirschwasser* or cherry brandy), so untypical of both wine and brandy, used to disguise the potent effects of the drink, or simply because of the innocuous appearance of the liquid? As to the word *vie* (life), it does indeed refer to the ability to increase bodily energy, to revive the victim of a heart attack or to revitalize the dying. Although the spirit obtained from the distillation of wine is generally known as brandy, the word *coñac* is more common in Spain and is derived from the Cognac district of France, where brandy was first distilled.

The art of distillation was discovered by the Arabs in the early Middle Ages, and the wine used for it is generally white and made in the same way as for table wines. In the wine museum at Vilafranca del Penedès (see page 19) there are exhibits illustrating the traditional process, and one can see stills or alembics dating from the thirteenth and fourteenth centuries. It is interesting that even today the upper part of the alembic, which collects the vapours of the boiling wine, is called the 'Moor's Head'.

In mediaeval times spirits were mainly employed in pharmacy, and the first use of brandy in medicine is ascribed to a celebrated Catalan doctor of the thirteenth century, Arnau de Vilanova, an adviser to the Anti-pope Clement V, who cultivated vines. With the passage of time distillers have perfected the art of making brandy for ordinary consumption by selecting the most suitable vines and distinguishing between the products from different districts.

Distillation

The object of distillation is to get rid of much of the water and to vapourize and collect the volatile components, which are thus concentrated; and this is done by boiling the wine. Involatile acids and colouring matter remain in the water at the end of the process.

The mediaeval alembic, in slightly modified form, remains the best apparatus for collecting the distillates of wine; and its use involves two stages, so that the process is called 'discontinuous'. It is also described as the *Charentais* method, since it was first employed in the Charente district of the French Cognac region.

The process can best be understood by reference to the accompanying diagram. The wine is first pumped into the kettle of the alembic (1), where it will be boiled, and coal or wood are shovelled through the doors (4) and lit by hand or mechanically. As the temperature rises in the kettle, the wine starts to boil, and the vapours pass slowly through the 'Moor's Head' and a pipe leading through the heating chamber (2), which has previously been charged with wine. The wine in the heating chamber soon reaches boiling point and begins distilling; and in the meantime the vapours are channelled into the condensor (3), which is simply a tank of cold water containing a long spiral coil. As the vapour from the wine passes through its serpentine tubes, it is cooled and finally condenses as liquid, which is collected in barrels and will later be re-distilled. During this first stage of distillation, wine with an original alcohol content of about 10° is converted into a *flema* (French, *brouilli*) with a strength of 30°.

In the second stage, the *flema* is returned to the kettle and undergoes a similar process, emerging as a spirit of 65° to 70°. The second distillation is a much more delicate operation than the first and must be carried out with great care; and in this lies the true art of making brandy. The distiller will continually check the product, rejecting the unwanted fractions, generally produced at the beginning and end of the process and known as the 'headings' and 'tailings'. Only the middle fraction or 'heart' is used for making brandy.

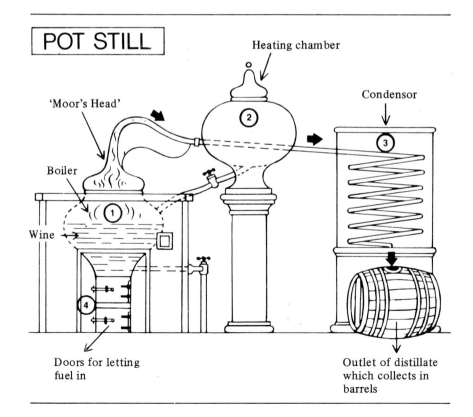

POT STILL

Heating chamber

Condensor

'Moor's Head'

Boiler

Wine

Doors for letting
fuel in

Outlet of distillate
which collects in
barrels

Rectifying columns of a 'continuous' still.

The distillate of wine is known in Spain as *Holandas,* because in the past Holland was a great importer of spirits; and *Holandas* can be made by another method which converts them into spirit in a single stage. The saving of time and fuel with this so-called 'continuous' process is considerable, but the quality of the product is always inferior. The equipment differs in employing powerful rectifying columns, permitting the production of spirit with an alcohol content of up to 96°. Wine of only moderate quality may be utilized with acceptable results, but although such spirit is authorized for the manufacture of brandy under Spanish regulations, it is never used for brandies of quality. Only wine of really good quality is used in the 'discontinuous' process; its delicate flavours will be faithfully retained, and the final spirit will be better balanced and more subtle. It is the only method used in the Cognac region and for most of the Penedès brandies.

The Ageing of Brandy

After distillation the spirit has an alcohol content of 65° to 70° and is completely colourless, and if it were to be stored in metal or glass-lined containers, there would be virtually no further development. However, in direct contact with oak and with the

177

passage of years, profound changes are wrought in the distillate or *alma del vino* ('soul of wine'):

1. The slow seepage of oxygen through the pores of the wood gradually ages the brandy.

2. The oak barrel imparts colour and tannic flavours to the brandy.

3. Each year, through natural evaporation, the alcoholic strength grows less, and the addition of small but precise amounts of water finally reduces it to about 40°.

4. Complicated changes, still not fully understood, take place, as a result of which harmony is achieved between the noble flavour of oak and the bouquet of the distillate. It finally loses its brashness and strength, maturing to perfection, and acquiring both softness and colour, and good balance. After many years it will be a true brandy, with deep overtones of colour and an infinite range of delicate aromas.

How to Serve Brandy

A clear balloon or tulip-shaped glass is called for. Always refuse a glass which has been pre-warmed; all that is necessary before savouring a brandy is to warm the glass gently in the hand. It is a solecism to drink brandy 'on the rocks' or to mix it with soft drinks. This is permissable with other less refined alcoholic beverages, but brandy, like wine, must be drunk on its own, without additions which spoil its delicate taste.

Unlike red wine, brandy does not improve once it has been bottled. Bottles should be stored upright, and there is nothing to be gained by keeping them for years.

Liqueurs Based on Brandy

Liqueurs are produced in infinite variety throughout the world, and many are made from brandy or wine. Those with a brandy base are usually made by infusing it with herbs, the rinds of fruit, especially oranges and lemons, or with honey. Others, based on wine alcohol, are made by macerating the fruit or herbs with the wine in the still, so that the vapours carry over their characteristic aromas.

Perhaps the best-known of Spanish-made liqueurs is Chartreuse. Originally made in France by the Carthusian monks of the Monastery of La Grande Chartreuse near Grenoble in 1764, it has had a long and romantic history; and in 1903, when the brothers were expelled from France, its fabrication was transferred to Tarragona. It is still made by the monks, and production is now shared between their distilleries at Voiron and at Tarragona.

CHAPTER XIV

Wine fraternities and harvest celebrations

During the Middle Ages *cofradías* or fraternities were often markedly religious in tenour, but this is not true of present-day wine fraternities, for all the lyrical enthusiam displayed during their rites. Their purpose is solely to uphold standards; wine is a bond of union, but can never be a religion, despite the fact that Christ chose it as a symbol of communion with his disciples. The fraternities with which we are concerned exist only to foster conviviality and the art of good living. And high spirits and friendship hardly amount to religion.

Their History

Since mediaeval times it has been the custom for those engaged in different crafts and trades to form guilds, which not only performed some of the functions of the modern trade union, but also had a deeper, symbolic purpose in linking the labourer with mother earth. In fraternities of eastern origin, the rites, first sexual and later funereal, were often linked with the cult of meteorites; and in classical Greece a large part was played by wine and its gods, Dionysus and Bacchus.

During the Middle Ages the cult of Dionysus was revived, and in Catalonia he was represented as wearing Lucifer's cape, made from the skin of a bull, and always with huge horns —a potent symbol in the western Mediterranean. Over the years these Dionysia degenerated into 'dances of the devils', still celebrated during the *fiestas* of most Catalan towns and an important part of traditional folklore.

Although the ancient fraternities finally achieved status and prestige, they were always of humble origin, stemming from the guilds of masons, potters, stone-cutters and others, or, as in the case of the Cofradía of San Miguel de las Viñas, from the simple farmers or *payeses,* who cultivated the Catalan vineyards.

Viticulture, which had become so important in Catalonia after its introduction by the Greeks and Romans, declined after the Moorish invasion (see page 17). It was revived after the Reconquest and especially in the twelfth century when Ramon Berenguer ('the Great') ordered the repopulation of the liberated territories and brought in from Provence specialists in the cultivation of the soil and the vine. In this connection it should be remembered that Provence and the Roussillon were then subject to the Counts of Barcelona, who later joined forces with the Kingdom of Aragón, incorporated with Castile to form the Kingdom of Spain only at the beginning of the sixteenth century. The last of the Spanish territories in the French Midi was lost in the eighteenth century, when the Pyrenees became the permanent frontier.

The castle of San Martí Sarroca, the venue for many meetings of the wine fraternities.

The great festival of the Cofradía of San Miguel de las Viñas is faithfully recorded in contemporary chronicles, which still survive and refer to the Fiesta de la Vendimia held during the last days of August or the first of September. In those authoritarian times, when tyranny and despotism were rife, there were few occasions on which the peasants could escape from the rigours of their life. This carnival was one of them, and for the Fraternity of San Miguel, it was above all the festival of the wine harvest. On this occasion even the Church, severe as it was, turned a blind eye to the revelries of the villagers.

Wine Fraternities of the World

In almost all the wine-producing countries the spontaneous emergence of such fraternities reflects the great social impact of wine. And in what better way can one make known the excellences of one's native wines than in these cheerful fraternities devoted to the arts of eating and drinking? They meet a social need with their functions, and by honouring distinguished visitors, from home and abroad, forge links between cities and countries. They are the ideal vehicle for encouraging the appreciation of wine, and more than that, for spreading warmth, fellowship and understanding among men of good will.

Because of her great wine tradition, France is the country which numbers most; in 1975 there were forty-five, of which the principal are:

Bordeaux:
Jurade de Saint-Emilion,
Demeure Historique du Girondin, 33330 Saint-Emilion (Gironde)
Compagnons du Bordeaux,
105, rue de Saint-Gènes, 33330 Bordeaux (Gironde)
Burgundy:
Confrèrie des Chevaliers du Tastevin,
Château du Clos Vougeot, 21700 Nuits-Saint-Georges (Cote d'Or)
Confrèrie des Vignerons de Saint-Vincent de Bourgogne et de
Macôn, 3 bis, rue Gambetta, 71000 Macôn (Saône-et-Loire)
Jura, Franche-Comté:
Paierie des grands vins d'Arbois, 39600 Arbois (Jura)
Roussillon:
Commande Majeure du Roussillon, Château Royal de Perpignan,
66000 Perpignan (Pyrénées Orientales)
Cognac:
Principauté de Franc-Pineau, 16100 Cognac (Charente)

Chevaliers du Tastevin (Burgundy).

Information about these and others can be obtained from the Institut National des Appellations d'Origine, 38 Av. Champs-Elysées, 75008 Paris.

Italy, Germany, Switzerland, Portugal, the United States, Canada, Australia and New Zealand also take pride in their wine fraternities, which hold regular meetings.

In Spain, wine fraternities, or societies with identical aims, exist in Galicia, the Rioja and Jerez de la Frontera, but it is perhaps in the Penedès, a district so open to cultural influences, that the fraternities have grown most rapidly. The three principal are:

La Academia de Tastavins de San Humbert, in Vilafranca del Penedès.
La Cofradía de San Miguel de las Viñas, also in Vilafranca del Penedès.
El Serenísimo Capítulo de Caballeros del Vino, in Barcelona.

The Chapter of a Wine Fraternity

Since the principal object of the fraternities is the promotion of wine, Chapters are usually held in honour of distinguished visitors associated in one way or another with wine. They are also linked with local festivals held in honour of their patron saints.

In Vilafranca del Penedès, the Cofradía de San Miguel de las Viñas organizes functions of both types as a pleasant means of encouraging the export and good name of Penedès wines, and from time to time carries out its ceremonies abroad.

The well-known writer Néstor Luján receives his diploma of membership at the Academia de Tastevins St. Humbert in Vilafranca.

The investiture ceremony of the Serenísimo Capítulo de Caballeros del vino in Barcelona.

The Chapter, or ceremony of installing new members of the fraternity, is a serious occasion, but at the same time cheerful and festive. After a dinner, in which honour has been done to the excellent Catalan food, the lights are extinguished and the chapter house is lit by flaming cressets. The Grand Constable, the Chancellor, the Grand Magistrate and the Consuls of the Fraternity enter to the strains of an ancient Catalan fanfare and ceremoniously take their places on the dais. With due solemnity the Grand Constable then declares the Chapter open and proceeds to explain the history and aims of the Fraternity.

This photograph and the two that follow were taken at a meeting of the Chapter of the Cofradía de San Miguel de las Viñas in the Penedès.

He recalls that, although the Fraternity dates from the fourteenth century, it fell into abeyance during the phylloxera oubreak of the nineteenth century and that only in 1970 were its age-long rites revived by a group of enthusiasts for Catalan wines. The Chancellor then takes over, speaking of the merits of the future knights, of their links with Catalan wines and of their eligibility for admission into the ranks of the Fraternity.

Next comes the liveliest and most interesting part of the Chapter, when the Grand Magistrate prescribes the *pruebas de rigor* (the strict tests) to be undergone by the neophyte before admission to the Fraternity. He warns the candidates of the dangers and tribulations that they face, and they must agree, come what may, to 'do or die' in the attempt. Having survived these *durísimas pruebas,* the aspirant pledges his solemn oath that he will faithfully love and respect the wines of Catalonia. On being informed of the dire consequences of drinking water, he also swears to renounce it for the rest of his days and finally promises to visit Vilafranca and its vineyards whenever occasion arises.

With due pomp and ceremony the Grand Constable now taps the shoulder of the new knight with a vine shoot, embraces him and presents him with his insignia: a silver *tastevin,* a mediaeval parchment and a Catalan hat, which he must guard zealously and display at future ceremonies.

When all the new brethren have thus been honoured, they share with the dignitaries who have invested them a chalice of red wine, ceremoniously passed from hand to hand. The Chapter has ended, but the celebrations continue long into the night.

Harvest Festivals

Old traditions linger on and find new expression today in the harvest festivals: for example, Sitges, the tourist capital of the Costa Dorada, celebrates its *Fiesta de la Vendimia* at the beginning of September. In memory of times past a fountain gushes free wine for the enjoyment of visitors and towns folk alike. The first ceremony is the naming of the Queen of the Harvest, who is duely crowned; then comes a service of thanksgiving, which, in Sitges, takes place in the old church of Nuestra Señora del Vinyet. In the presence of the bishop, the civic authorities and a crowded congration, the Queen, attended by her maids of honour, presses a few bunches of grapes

The Queen of the Wine Harvest presses the first bunch of grapes.

—the first of the year— and the juice pours into an ancient silver chalice and is blessed with due solemnity. The rest of the day is given over to an elaborate round of celebrations in honour of wine.

Throughout the whole of Spain, September and October are a time of rejoicing for vineyard workers, growers, artists and all lovers of good wine. It is then that regions so blessed by nature celebrate their good fortune and share with all who visit them their great treasure, wine.

VINE CULTIVATION IN THE WORLD

VINEYARD AREAS (1000 ha.)

COUNTRY	AVERAGE 1973-1977	1978	1979	YEAR 1979 Vineyards in production	New vineyards
WORLD-WIDE	10 239	10 180	10 171		
EUROPE	7 333	7 289	7 264		
Albania	13	12			
Austria	50	56	56	49	7
Bulgaria	195	181	...	156	25
Czechoslovakia	41	43	43	35	8
France	1 295	1 214	1 225	1 172	53
Greece	200	194	...	188	7
Hungary	204	186	174	154	20
Italy	1 391	1 386	1 379	1 332	47
Luxembourg	1	1	1	—	—
Malta	1	1	1	—	—
Portugal	358	390	...	388	2
Rumania	319	290	...	...	...
Spain	1 712	1 719	...	1 624	95
Switzerland	14	13	13	13	
U.S.S.R.	1 193	1 254	...	845	409
Yugoslavia	247	247	246	227	19
AMERICA	920	939	955		
Argentina	346	356	366	363	3
Bolivia	3	4	4	—	—
Brazil	63	59*	59*	...	...
Canada	12	25*	25*		
Chile	121	116		107	9
Mexico	38	52	58	51	7
Peru	14	11*	11*	—	—
United States:					
California	258	261	...	...	...
Other States	39	39	...	...	...
Uruguay	22	12*	12*	—	—
Other countries	4	4	4*	—	—

PRODUCTION (in 1000 hl)

COUNTRY	AVERAGE 1973-1977	1978	1979	INCREASE OR DECREASE 1978-1979	
WORLD-WIDE	322 941	295 858	368 530	+	72 672
EUROPE	255 476	232 284	298 575	+	66 291
Albania	200	210*	210*	—	
Austria	2 608	3 366	2 773	—	593
Belgium	5	4	4	—	
Bulgaria	3 361	2 731	...	—	
Czechoslovakia	1 298	1 390	1 442	+	52
France	69 852	58 170	83 543	+	25 373
Greece	5 353	5 605	5 300*	—	305
Hungary	5 094	4 913	5 186	+	273
Italy	71 815	72 439	84 337	+	11 898
Luxembourg	136	72	63	—	9
Malta	27	15*	15*	—	
Portugal	10 109	6 594	11 498	+	4 904
Rumania	8 028	7 850	...	—	
Spain	34 262	29 031	50 582	+	21 551
Switzerland	971	778	1 108	+	330
U.S.S.R.	27 596	25 929	27 000*	+	1 071
Yugoslavia	6 238	5 880	6 742	+	862
AMERICA	48 979	48 103	53 306	+	5 203
Argentine	24 971	21 318	26 950	+	5 632
Bolivia	9	20*	20*	—	
Brazil	2 239	2 850*	2 850*	—	
Canada	575	390*	380*	—	
Chile	5 560	5 612	5 506	—	106
Mexico	150	150	...	—	
Peru	80	90	90*	—	
United States:					
California	14 437	17 123	16 800*	—	323
Other States					
Uruguay	838	450*	450*	—	
Other countries	100	100	100	—	

COUNTRY	AVERAGE 1973-1977	TOTAL CONSUMPTION (1000 hl)			PER HEAD	
		1978	1979	Difference	1978	1979
WORLD-WIDE	286 495	291 925	291 801	− 124		
EUROPE	233 464	232 606	233 332	+ 726		
Austria	2 688	2 631	2 962	+ 331	35.00	39.50
Belgium	1 507	1 665	1 868	+ 203	16.92	18.99
Bulgaria	1 738	1 850*	1 850*	−	22.00*	22.00*
Czechoslovakia	1 681	1 800*	1 800*	−	11.89	11.89
Denmark	559	583	656	+ 73	11.44	12.86
East Germany	1 181	1 350*	1 350*	−	8.10*	8.10*
Finland	280	219	219	−	4.61	4.62
France	54 172	52 408	50 681	− 1 727	96.29	92.61
Greece	3 348	3 690	...	−	42.00	...
Holland	3 604	3 810	...	−	34.00	...
Hungary	84	142	...	−	4.40	...
Italy	57 951	51 597	...	−	91.00	...
Low Countries	1 328	1 637	1 625	12	11.74	11.66
Luxembourg	156	156	142	− 14	43.30	40.00
Norway	129	118	...	−	2.92	
Poland	2 593	3 256	...	−	9.30	...
Portugal	7 983	8 947	...	−	91.30	...
Rumania	6 859	7 232	...	−	33.10	...
Spain	26 222	25 746	...	−	70.00	...
Sweden	682	749	788	+ 39	9.06	9.13
Switzerland	2 833	2 856	2 874	+ 18	45.14	45.42
United Kingdom	2 986	2 978	...	+ 1 908	5.30	...
U.S.S.R.	33 000	36 624	...	−	14.00	...
West Germany	13 811	15 004	14 911	− 93	24.40	24.30
Yugoslavia	6 089	5 558	...	−	25.37	...

IMPORTS (1000 hl)

COUNTRY	1978	1979	DIFFERENCE 1978-1979	
WORLD-WIDE	41 706	46 195	+	4 489
EUROPE	34 780	38 820	+	4 040
Austria	261	233	−	28
Belgium	1 922	2 054	+	132
Bulgaria	122	...	−	
Czechoslovakia	375	312	−	63
Denmark	633	696	+	63
East Germany	1 300	...	−	
Finland	125	111	−	14
France	7 455	8 470	+	1 015
Greece	5*	5*	−	
Holland	1 644	1 742	+	78
Hungary	214	214	−	
Ireland	101	117	ı	16
Italy	236	231	−	5
Luxembourg	84	147	+	63
Malta	22	22	−	
Norway	115	...	−	
Poland	450*	...	−	
Portugal	1*	1*	−	
Rumania	1*	1*	−	
Spain	22	9	−	63
Sweden	738	805	+	67
Switzerland	1 899	1 974	+	75
United Kingdom	3 767	4 671	+	904
U.S.S.R.	5 910	...	−	
West Germany	7 352	9 100	+	1 748
Yugoslavia	6	8	+	2

EXPORTS (in 1000 hl)

COUNTRY	AVERAGE 1973-1977	1978	1979	DIFFERENCE 1978-1979	
WORLD-WIDE	42 949	42 283	52 523	+	10 240
EUROPE	34 821	36 476	47 099	+	10 623
Albania	113	134	...	—	
Austria	187	240	443	+	195
Belgium	110	257	186	—	71
Bulgaria	2 330	2 434	...	—	
Czechoslovakia	15	29	49	+	20
Denmark	10	19	15	— —	
France	7 030	7 591	8 541	+	950
Holland	34	25	26	+	1
Greece	989	1 120	...	—	
Hungary	1 683	2 050	2 260	+	210
Italy	12 301	13 557	19 979	+	6 422
Luxembourg	76	73	74	+	1
Malta	60	77	...	—	
Portugal	1 909	1 346	1 474	+	128
Rumania	964	1 000*	...	—	
Switzerland	7	8	7	—	1
Spain	5 028	3 751	6 098	+	2 347
United Kingdom	132	214	220	+	6
U.S.S.R.	127	140*	...	—	
West Germany	885	1 480	1 642	+	162
Yugoslavia	751	843	1 100	+	257
Other countries	80	80	80	—	
AMERICA	415	937	460	—	447
Argentina	242	675	88	—	587
Chile	67	107	...	—	
United States	50	86	195	+	109
Other countries	56	69	70	+	1

BIBLIOGRAPHY

Amerine, M.A., Bergeret, M.S. and Cruess, S.A., *Technology of Wine Making,* Avi Publishing Co. Inc. (U.S.A.).

Apollinaire, Guillaume, *Larousse des vins,* Librairie Larousse, Paris.

Bergeret, J., various publications, University of Dijon.

Born, Wina, *The Concise Atlas of Wine,* Charles Scribner & Sons, New York.

Castillo, José del. *Los vinos de España,* Editorial Proyección, Bilbao, 1971.

Codina, J. de, *De cómo conocer, comprender, apreciar, servir y elegir bien los vinos,* Coullert, Madrid.

Dumay, Raymond, *Guide du vin,* Brodard et Taupin, Paris.

Garoglio, P.G., *La nuova enologia,* Instituto di Industrie Agrarie, Florence.

Guillete, Peter A. and Paul, *Playboy's Book of Wine,* Playboy Press, Chicago.

Johnson, Hugh, *Wine,* 1982 ed., London, 1976.
The World Atlas of Wine, 2nd ed., London, 1977.

Klieve, H., *Wein und Gesundheit,* Verlag D. Meininger, Neustadt.

Kressman, E., *Le guide des vins et des vignobles de France,* Edouard E. Isavier Sequoia, Brussels.

Lucia, S.P., *Wine as Good as Medicine,* Blakiston Co. Inc., New York.

Marcilla Arrazola, J., *Tratado práctico de viticultura y enología española,* Madrid (Vol. I, *Viticultura,* 1963; Vol. II, *Enología,* 1967).

Maury, E.A., *Soignez-vous par le vin,* Jean Pierre Delarge, Paris.

Pedraza, M. and Jesús, F., *El Mundo de los vinos y bebidas internacionales,* Madrid.

Pérez, J. and Alsina, R., *Diccionario de vinos españoles,* Editorial Teide, Barcelona.

Poupon, Pierre, *Nouvelles pensées d'un dégustateur,* Confrérie des Chevaliers du Tastevin, Dijon.

Quittanson, Charles, *Connaissance et gloire du vin,* Editions Brès, Paris.

Read, Jan, *The Wines of Spain and Portugal,* Faber and Faber, London, 1973.

Ribéreau Gayon, J. and Peynaud E., *Traité d'oenologie,* Librairie Polytechnique Béranger, Paris.

Simon, André, *Wines of the World,* McGraw Hill Publishing Co., New York, new ed., 1981.

Reay-Smith, J., *Discovering Spanish Wine,* Robert Hale, London, 1976.

Snyder, C.R., *Alcohol and the Jews, a Cultural Study of Drinking and Sobriety,* New Haven.

Torbert, Harold, C., *The Book of Wine,* Nash Publishing, Los Angeles.

Vila San Juan, J.F., *Alacena y bodega,* Plaza y Janés. Barcelona.

Wine Advisory Board (of California), *Uses of Wine in Medical Practice,* San Francisco.

Note. Dates of publication should be added where missing.

CONTENTS